Possessed by God

Titles in this series:

THE
TUESDAY

THE NONSUCH KING

Benjamin J. Myers

Orion
Children's Books

First published in Great Britain in 2011
by Orion Children's Books
a division of the Orion Publishing Group Ltd
Orion House
5 Upper St Martin's Lane
London WC2H 9EA
An Hachette UK company

1 3 5 7 9 10 8 6 4 2

A catalogue record for this book
is available from the British Library.

ISBN 978 1 84255 642 9

Typeset by Input Data Services Ltd,
Bridgwater, Somerset

Printed in Great Britain by
Clays Ltd, St Ives plc

The Orion Publishing Group's policy is to use papers that
are natural, renewable and recyclable products made from
wood grown in sustainable forests. The logging and
manufacturing processes are expected to conform to
the environmental regulations of the country of origin.

www.orionbooks.co.uk

To Betty and Bertha

CHAPTER 1

The girl hung, suspended in the air, arms outstretched, cruciform. A pillar of blue smoke spiralled up from the floor to each wrist, as if drawing her arms apart. Her heels dangled loosely, a metre above the floor tiles. Her chin rested on her chest, silver-yellow curls slewn over her face. She was eleven years old. She had been eleven years old for one hundred and fifty-eight years, ever since Julius had found her. Her name was Samphire and she was a Blood Sentinel.

As footsteps snapped towards her, the girl lifted her head and peered into the gloom of the huge library. The candle-faint security lights on the wall barely broke the dark cliff-faces of the shelves that loomed across the room, almost to the high glass roof. The walls were constructed of reinforced glass too, but tonight it was impossible to see by the illumination of the adjacent tower blocks. Curtains of rain swung out of the sky, slashing across the roof and about the glass walls. Up here, forty glass and steel floors above the city streets, Samphire might as well have been out at sea.

'I did not expect the three of us to meet again,' said

the man in the beige overcoat. His thighs were level with Samphire's feet but he was not speaking to her; he did not even look at her. The shoulders and back of his coat were soaked, and water dripped from it to the floor, gathering in a pool about his black, patent leather shoes. He removed a trilby, smacked rainwater from it and ran a hand through his slick, steel hair.

'Three of us?' queried the woman in the scarlet, plastic coat, who approached from the shadows. 'You didn't say that Tethys would be coming.'

'Oriana,' crooned Fenley Ravillious, chairman of the CREX Corporation, the Twisted Symmetry's earthly crime network, and one of the Twisted Symmetry's twelve Crystal Priests; their most powerful human servants. 'How could you expect me to attend without my daughter?'

'Daughter?' The woman in the scarlet coat drew closer, stiletto heels stabbing the floor, brown hair tied back in a tight bun, high, porcelain cheeks flushed: Dr Oriana Lache, a director of CREX, admired globally for her charitable work, but no less a Crystal Priest than Fenley Ravillious. 'That freak you call a daughter isn't even human.'

'She came from me, in part.' Fenley Ravillious permitted his tawny, parchment face to crack a slight smile. 'That is human enough.' He looked up at Samphire and the Blood Sentinel's lustrous green eyes shone back, despite the pain in her arms.

Fenley Ravillious sniffed. 'You were right to call me, Oriana.' His voice crackled with self-assured power. 'The Committee's assassins must be handled with care.' He smiled up at the Blood Sentinel, pitifully. 'Yet they never learn;

always the Committee seek to thwart the Symmetry in our quest for eternal life.'

'Quest for universal death, more like,' interjected Samphire.

Ravillious ignored her totally. 'And always, they fail. But nevertheless, they must be handled with care. They are ... slippery.'

'Soo Chen is dead.' Oriana tossed the words at Ravillious, waiting to see the reaction. 'A Crystal Priest like us, Fenley, and now she is dead.'

'I know. Very unfortunate. For her. Doubtless the work of the Committee. Now the Inquisitors are seeking a successor for Behrens, seeking a fresh Inquisitor, all of us are targets. After all, the obvious candidate will be a Crystal Priest, one of our twelve.' He coughed neatly as he corrected his mistake. 'Or should I say, in the light of Soo Chen's demise, eleven.'

'But the assassin used a Jericho bean.' Dr Lache's high voice quavered slightly.

'How very unpleasant, for Soo Chen,' purred the chairman of CREX.

'That's not what I mean, Fenley. The Committee's assassins don't use Jericho beans.' Dr Lache straightened her elegant shoulders. 'But the Symmetry's do.'

'Then we must all be very careful, Oriana,' smiled Fenley Ravillious. 'After all, the stakes are now extremely high. I like to think that we can trust one another, but who knows what someone might do to seize the opportunity created by Behrens's destruction?'

His head cocked to one side as he caught the soft footsteps

that approached from the murk. 'Ah good, here comes my daughter.'

A hooded figure padded out of the long throat of the library, black skiing jacket shining wet. In front of Ravillious, the figure stopped, pulled back the hood and lowered her head, allowing her father to cup her gaunt cheeks between his hands and tilt her broad white brow forwards so that he could kiss it. Then she turned her wide face towards Dr Lache and stared, unblinking.

Dr Lache regarded the chalk skin stretched so tight over bone that the purple veins beneath stood clear as a dissection, the thin strands of oily black hair that clung to the scalp like weeds, the big, soulless eyes with drilling violet irises, and she stifled a shudder.

'Hello, Tethys,' said the doctor.

Tethys stared back and said nothing.

'With the passing of Soo Chen, eleven Crystal Priests remain.' As Fenley Ravillious spoke, Dr Lache noted the way that his eyes caught his daughter's and, not for the first time, she sensed that thoughts passed between them which remained unknown to her. 'Of those eleven, only three have the capacity to replace Behrens.' Ravillious turned his eyes on Dr Lache now. 'You, me and Keppler.' He shook his head as if sad. 'I would have included Soo Chen, but for her unfortunate demise. Of course, you and I both had the chance to please our masters with a gift of the girl, Chess Tuesday. But we both failed.'

'She was very hard to catch,' insisted the doctor, her high cheeks reddening. 'She is sly. And she is powerful.' Her voice dropped, catching hoarsely. 'She killed Behrens.' Ravillious's contemptuous gaze spurred her on. '*You* and your traders couldn't catch her. Not even the Symmetry's own forces could catch her, and the Sentinels are watching over her now. Time is running out and the Inquisitors are doing nothing.'

'Be careful, Oriana.' Ravillious's lizard eyes narrowed. 'Our masters don't welcome criticism.' He smiled dangerously. 'Perhaps I have more faith in them than you do. It is true that the girl has evaded them thus far. She has created problems. The destruction of the cerebral torus by Miss Tuesday and her gang of delinquents has been ... inconvenient. Without the brain to assist in the transport of children, energy cannot be harvested as it has been before.' Ravillious waved his hand dismissively. 'But this is not an insurmountable problem. The Symmetry has vast stockpiles of energy. Nine months from now, the time spiral will reach the fifth node. *Then* we shall see how the Inquisitors bend the girl to their will.'

'But how will they get her?' Dr Lache's neatly defined jaw muscles clenched with frustration.

'I think you will find that where Chess Tuesday is concerned, the Inquisitors have adopted a fresh strategy.' Ravillious raised a hand to Samphire's foot. 'Brute force is not the only way to obtain what we want.' He rested his nails where the Sentinel's bare ankle emerged from her jeans, and stroked them across her skin. 'We must learn from our mistakes. It would have been better to coordinate our efforts. Being in competition with one another is unhelpful.'

'Which is why I let you know we had caught this assassin.' Dr Lache studied the hanging girl as if seeing her for the first time. 'We had reports that she was on her own and moving through the city.' The doctor's long fingers adjusted her horn spectacles, then touched the short necklace she wore at her throat. They brushed over the silvery pendant cast in the shape of a C with three minute stars at its centre, the symbol of the CREX Corporation; the symbol which appeared on the ring worn by Ravillious and also on the ring worn by Tethys.

'We observed her enter the Institute building and make her way up here, to the library. She thought she went unseen.' Dr Lache looked directly at Samphire. 'But we see *everything*.' She indicated the smoking columns which bound Samphire's wrists. 'Satisfied that she was alone, I summoned the xenrian gaolers.'

'Very wise,' agreed Ravillious. 'It is always safest to lock the subatomic structure of these pan-dimensional creatures; to prevent them from slipping away.' He regarded Samphire thoughtfully. 'What were you looking for, I wonder? What brought you to the CREX Research Institute? There are so many books in this city, and so many libraries, I wonder why our little assassin was sent to steal *here*?'

'I am not an assassin.' Samphire's voice was as clear as spring water.

'Of course not,' Ravillious croaked in mock-sympathy. 'You are a Blood Sentinel. Your blood has been mixed with the blood of that misguided and mildly sociopathic immortal, Julius, and now you fight, nobly, to defend the universe. But you see, my little paladin,' and here Ravillious motioned towards the twisting, vaporous gaolers, '*your* good deeds invariably end in the death of one of *our* brethren.' The blue smoke shrank so quickly that Samphire's knees slammed to the floor. Now she was kneeling before the three Crystal Priests. 'It is all about point of view. And from our point of view, you are one of the villains.'

Rain swirled about the tower, thrashing the glass. In every direction, the rest of the city was a spattered blur of pin-prick lights.

'There are two pieces of information we require.' Fenley Ravillious rested a hand on Samphire's curls. She moved to push it away, but the smoking coils of the xenrian gaolers held her wrists fast. Inside her body, the gaolers infiltrated her sub-atomic fields, preventing her from shifting through the dimensions, to a time or place away from her captors.

'First, you will tell us what you were looking for. You are Julius's pet thief. That is why he recruited you. We would like to know what it is that has so aroused the Committee's interest.' The Crystal Priest's well manicured hand slipped under Samphire's chin, wrenching it up so that she had to look at him. 'And, second, you will tell us where Julius is to be found. You will tell us where he walks alone, where he sleeps, where he is most vulnerable. A gift of his body to the Inquisitors would be of immense assistance to me,' and, after the briefest of hesitations, he added, 'as doubtless it would be to Dr Lache.'

'I will tell you ...'

'Nothing, I know,' interrupted Fenley Ravillious, wearily. He turned his back on Samphire and walked into the shadows contemplatively, shoes smudging the pool of rainwater that had collected from his sodden coat. 'It is often the case that nobody says anything, until we *make* them.'

'I won't feel the pain.' Samphire's eyes glittered in the half-light. 'My neurotransmitters ...'

'Can be blocked by your own will, I know, I know,' murmured Ravillious, 'which is why we have had to think creatively.'

Dr Lache opened the small handbag that was slung from her shoulder and took out a syringe.

'Please, doctor, tell the assassin what we shall use.' Ravillious returned from the shadows, a hint of a frown creasing his brow. He cast a glance at Tethys who then looked about the yawning darkness of the library before closing her eyes.

'Dream,' explained the doctor, 'is a potent, psychotropic drug.'

'Which means it plays tricks on the mind,' interrupted Ravillious. 'Apologies, Oriana. Please, continue.'

'Obviously, in its pure form, it is illegal. But, as part of CREX's pharmaceutical enterprise, it is manufactured and distributed globally, on a massive scale. It assists us in our work. No government that knows about it objects; how could they?' The doctor allowed herself one of her sparse smiles. 'There is too much money to be made.'

'It is the principal ingredient in a number of *lawful* medicines,' observed Ravillious. 'It would be foolish for the authorities to object to the mass production of Dream. It would be *inhumane* of them.'

Oriana Lache weighed the syringe in her open palm. 'The primary effect of Dream is to induce and enhance delusions; the user will be convinced that their desires, their fears, their beliefs are true, however ludicrous. Give enough to a beggar and he will believe he is a billionaire; his rags will be robes, his fingernails, gold coins.' Dr Lache held the syringe and squirted a tiny jet of clear liquid into the air. 'I believe that in this way, CREX actually increases the sum total of happiness in the world.'

'Is that a delusion?' asked Samphire, eyes sparkling innocently.

'I would kill her. Slowly.' Tethys spoke in a voice that was lifeless, cold as a morgue.

'Not now, child.' Ravillious placed a hand over his daughter's arm. 'Not yet.'

Rainwater swirled over the roof and gushed down the glass walls, patterning the inside of the glass library with an aquarium glimmer.

'One side-effect of Dream is that it loosens the mind, loosens the tongue.' The needle approached Samphire's neck, just above the collar of her black bomber jacket. 'This is a heavy dose. In less than a minute, you will tell us whatever we want to know. You will *want* to tell us. You will beg to betray your friends.'

Samphire's struggle showed only in her eyes; her body was held rigid. She could not avoid the tip of the needle.

Ravillious moistened his lips. Tethys's face remained blank, but she twitched her head, as if catching a sound in the distance. Then she said, 'Be quick,' and in answer to her father's quizzical glance, 'Maybe. Maybe.'

But when the needle was almost touching Samphire's skin, Oriana Lache's arm began to tremble and the doctor stared at it, jaw working, head shaking.

'I ... can't ... move ... my arm,' she gasped. 'Something's got hold of it.'

As Oriana Lache worked to move her arm, a large hand materialised on her wrist. With the hand there appeared an arm and then the rest of a body. Now, where there had been empty space beside the doctor, there stood a giant of a man. His head was crowned by short, carroty hair and his thick, ginger beard foamed down to the chest of his denim dungarees. In one hand he held a great staff of wood, shod with iron and in the other, Dr Lache's wrist.

'Ragg!' snarled Fenley Ravillious. 'I knew it.'

Tethys opened her eyes wide and the violet irises flamed. Instantly, a bookcase spun from its moorings and hurtled towards the man with the ginger beard.

'Wait!' Ravillious snapped at his daughter, and the bookcase toppled to the floor as if it had been dropped, books and journals spraying into the air like playing cards.

Slowly, Ravillious smiled at the man who had hold of Dr Lache's wrist. 'Is this it?'

From behind the wooden, double doors that spanned floor to ceiling at the far end of the library chamber, there came the roar of an engine. It rose in pitch, high throttle, then cut dead.

'Let go,' hissed Oriana Lache. But the giant with the ginger hair manacled her arm in his rock grip.

Footsteps approached the double doors and then, with a crash of splintering wood, the panels burst apart and a dwarf in a half-shell motorbike helmet and toting a pump-action shotgun was outlined in the gaping doorway. His shadow reached to the centre of the library, pointing towards the

Crystal Priests. Behind him stood a motorbike, glinting like a chrome skeleton.

Dr Lache was panting slightly from her struggle with the man in the dungarees, but Fenley Ravillious surveyed the rescue party coolly. 'Two Blood Sentinels? Only two?' He unbuttoned his overcoat so that it hung loose, and cast his trilby to the floor. 'You're sweating, Ragg. I don't suppose you expected me or my daughter to be here.' He sighed and shook his head. 'Poor planning, Ragg, poor planning.'

'We have come for Samphire,' said Ragg, whose voice was mellower than might have been expected from his giant frame.

'You don't say?' Ravillious smoothed back his sleek hair, then cracked his fingers. His eyes met his daughter's and although she was motionless as stone, the veins beneath her translucent skin darkened and pulsed. Then he turned his flint eyes back on the ginger-bearded hulk. 'Are you ready to die, Vladivostok Ragg?'

Ragg's skin was waxy, with florid blotches on his forehead and cheeks. It was covered by a sheen of sweat that darkened his fringe and plastered it flat. 'On this occasion, we might all withdraw, like a truce, if you order the gaolers to release Samphire.'

'Really?' Ravillious flicked a speck of dust from his shirt cuff. 'Enlighten me, Vladivostok Ragg, what exactly do *we* get out of this ambitious proposition?'

From the end of the library came the sound of a shotgun being cocked.

As Ragg shouted, 'Jake. No!' the dwarf growled, 'Damage.'

Up swung the nose of the gun and it flashed with a roar.

—[11]—

Tethys jerked her head towards the discharge, closed her eyes and held up her palms, fingers spread. The air rippled between the dwarf and the Priests, swallowing the spray of pellets. At the same time, Vladivostok Ragg swung Dr Lache like a doll, away from Samphire. The doctor wheeled through the air towards the nearest block of shelves, but before her body struck them, it stopped upside down and then righted itself, descending gracefully, stilettos first, syringe still in hand.

Feeling into the air with her other hand, the doctor tore the space in front of Ragg so that the Blood Sentinel started to slide into a cross-dimensional gap that shouldn't have been there. His free hand dived to his boot and he snatched out a knife. He flung it through the air and it thumped through the doctor's hand, pinning it to the bookcase and breaking her concentration. By the time she had pulled it free and organised the anatomy so as to repair the damage, Ragg had climbed back from the vortex.

The shotgun was blasting as the biker dwarf advanced. Tethys neutralised it by setting up a vectral loop, which cast the incoming shot away in an arc. The deflected pellets smashed into the library walls, cartridge after cartridge, pane after pane, the glass crashing down like immense walls of frost.

Ravillious focused his attention on Ragg. Reconfiguring the molecular structure of the air immediately in front of him so that it remained transparent but became as impenetrable as granite, he protected himself from gunshot. Simultaneously, he sought to divide the spatial matrix between the giant man and the glass wall of the library. He knew that Blood Sentinels operated mainly by speed and skill. They possessed some dimensional control but it was nothing compared with that by which the Inquisitors gifted their Priests. By distorting the time-space fabric through which Ragg moved, Ravillious planned to disorientate him. Then he and Tethys, or Dr Lache, could strike fatally. The crystal knife felt cold against his skin, through the silk of his shirt.

But Ragg was a seasoned adversary and however Fenley Ravillious tried to confuse him by twisting the floor, heaving down the roof, blotting out space, swallowing segments of time, the Blood Sentinel moved in perfect anticipation of the Crystal Priest's distortions, hurdling the dissolving fabric of the library and diving through the time gaps he opened.

Samphire watched as the glass shell of the library vanished about her, blown away by the shotgun barrage, bent out of existence by Ravillious in his efforts to confuse Vladivostok Ragg. Rain stormed down, lashing the naked chamber, soaking her through her clothes and whirring about the dissolving walls as the Blood Sentinels and the Crystal Priests battled, high in the city night.

Then she saw Oriana Lache collapse the distance between Vladivostok Ragg and the shattered outer wall of the library, sending the big man tumbling towards it, and she realised that simultaneously, Ravillious was re-plotting the geometric coordinates of the section of the floor to which he was sliding, tilting it steeply, removing the last traces of any wall. Unable to right himself against the coordinated chaos of the Crystal Priests, Ragg slid towards the edge of the floor, towards the drop.

'No!' screamed Samphire. This was not the plan. This had gone wrong. Badly wrong. 'Jake!' she yelled to the Gun Toting Biker Dwarf.

Jake was down to his last cartridge, but he needed only one. He had thrown so much lead at Tethys that he had been able to gauge the exact trajectory of the vectral loop; he could judge exactly how his shot would be thrown off-course. He pumped the final cartridge into the breach and aimed not at Tethys, but into the space five metres to her left.

The gun barked and the ball of shot swirled in a tight arc, caught by the loop. It hurtled in, behind Tethys, striking her right shoulder. She spun to the floor, clutching at the wound with her left hand.

Jake couldn't help Ragg, whose body was tumbling over the high lip of the tower, but he could finish this job before the Crystal Priest healed herself. Throwing away the shotgun, he took up a long shard of glass from where it lay on the wet floor.

Ragg slid into the air, two hundred and fifty metres above the streets. But to Samphire's surprise, he didn't fall.

'No!' Ravillious commanded Jake, whilst holding Ragg's body in suspension in the night sky.

Nobody moved. Everybody watched. The rain coursed down, soaking them all as they stood amidst the remains of the library.

'Let Tethys heal herself,' said the Crystal Priest, 'and I shall return Ragg to you.'

A musical box tune rang faintly in the silence. Everybody turned to look at Oriana Lache.

'It might be important,' she said to Ravillious.

He sighed heavily. 'Go on.'

Everybody waited as Dr Lache extracted a silver mobile phone from her handbag. She flicked a loose strand of brown hair away from her face as she spoke into the device. 'What? . . . A burglar? . . . A boy? No, no, don't kill him, Boulevant. Not yet. I can always find a use for children . . . I don't care how sneaky he looks. I'll deal with him when I get back home . . . Alright, kill him if he tries, but *only* if he tries; I enjoy administering the last rites myself.'

She snapped shut the phone. 'Sorry,' she muttered to Ravillious, flicking away wet hair again.

Jake dropped to a knee, the jagged glass against Tethys's throat. Tethys didn't flinch, although the veins in her skull-face pulsed harder, the strands of black hair drawn flat and meagre as squiggles across her white scalp. He nodded towards the body, suspended in the air. 'Ragg first. Then free Samphire.'

'Step back.' Ravillious waited until Jake had backed away from Tethys before he closed the gap between Vladivostok Ragg and the edge of the tower. The huge Blood Sentinel rolled onto the floor with a gasp.

'*Samphire*,' repeated Jake. He could see that already, Tethys had reconstructed her shattered shoulder. She looked up at her father who, in turn, glanced at Dr Lache. Dr Lache strode to where Ravillious stood, an arm's length from Samphire.

'I release her,' said Ravillious with a click of his fingers, and the xenrian gaolers vanished. Samphire, who had been unbowed until now, gave a sob and fell onto her hands. Water ran down her hair in streams.

—[15]—

Ragg noticed Tethys nod towards her father, saw the Crystal Priest slip his hand inside his shirt.

'I release her,' whispered Ravillious, 'into *eternity*.'

Vladivostok Ragg started forwards. But Tethys and Dr Lache had already grasped Samphire's arms, pulling them apart again. The crystal knife thudded home, deep into Samphire's chest. It was withdrawn swift as a snake strike, leaving a wound that cut through time and space and from which there could never be escape.

As the Blood Sentinels dashed forwards, the Crystal Priests backed away in a knot; Lache, pale and hard, Tethys blank, Ravillious with lips curled, triumphant.

'No,' grunted Jake, gripping Ragg's wrist hard enough to pull him back from the Priests, despite their difference in size. 'Samphire needs us.'

They turned to the girl, and Jake knelt beside her, propping up her limp body.

'It's so cold,' Samphire was saying, eyelids heavy. 'Cold to my bones.'

'A feeble display,' sneered Fenley Ravillious, flanked by Dr Lache and Tethys.

'It wasn't our best plan,' coughed Samphire, and she smiled as her eyes closed.

'It's not over,' Vladivostok Ragg shouted through the rain, staff in hand.

'Oh, Mr Ragg,' smiled Fenley Ravillious, tucking the crystal knife back inside his shirt, 'I think it is.' He smoothed back his hair and began to button his overcoat. 'No human can stand against the Symmetry. No human can defeat their Priests; not even a Blood Sentinel.'

He put an arm about his stone-faced daughter's fully repaired shoulder. 'Go to your burglar, Oriana,' and then, caustically, 'I am sure you can handle one boy.' He looked at the Blood Sentinels and the small body slumped at their feet and he smiled slowly before saying, 'He will be no match for the Symmetry.'

CHAPTER 2

Oriana Lache stepped quickly across the deep carpet, throwing her scarlet coat onto a white sofa and releasing her long, brown hair so that she could squeeze the water out of it. With her back to the crackling wood fire, she was facing the window that filled one wall and gave a view over the lake. By day she would have been able to see the dark-green pine woods, reflected so sharply that it was difficult to tell where the trees ended and the water began. Even now, despite the downpour, a musk-honeyed catch of resin lay beneath the tang of burning wood and the subtler shades of her perfume. But out here, at the western edge of the forests known as the Lungs, beyond the western rim of the city, night enveloped the lake, trees, sky and earth in absolute blackness and transformed the huge window into a perfect mirror.

Head on one side as she squeezed, Dr Lache saw reflected the short, rotund figure of Boulevant, pistol in hand and, in front of the fire, a boy. He must have been about fifteen years old. His face was long and pale, sharply boned with eyes that required watching, and his hair was slick and black and tied in a ponytail. His hands were clasped behind his back.

'Why are you gaping like a fish, Boulevant?'

After the trauma of fighting Blood Sentinels at the top of the CREX Institute, and the nerve-shearing tension of being near to Ravillious and his freakish progeny, she had no appetite for her companion's breathless flapping. 'I'm surprised you didn't shoot him at once.'

This was said for effect. She had given Boulevant orders not to kill the intruder; the kick to be enjoyed by absorbing his energy herself was too great to forego by a quick death.

'I was about to shoot him,' flustered Boulevant, 'but you came back. I've only just found him, snooping about.'

'I wasn't snooping about,' said the boy, very calmly. 'I was standing right here. I was waiting for you, Dr Lache.'

'Be quiet,' said Dr Lache, watching the boy in the night's mirror. He was nearly as tall as she was. He should have been more frightened. But she was distracted by Boulevant's ridiculous babbling.

'What do you mean, "just found him"? You rang me, nearly an hour ago.' Oriana Lache turned round now, winding her damp hair back onto her head, black dress wet from where it had been hanging.

Boulevant shook his flabby face, with its receding, curly grey hair and clown-like features. 'Didn't ring. Didn't have time,' he assured the doctor.

Dr Lache removed her spectacles, wiped condensation from the lenses with a tissue from the Juliette sleeve of her dress and sat down, crossing one stockinged leg over the other. '*Somebody* rang me.'

Boulevant shrugged, his yellow waistcoat rising up his

neat, round hump of a belly. Then he pushed the pistol closer to the boy. 'Shall I shoot?'

'What's your name?' asked Dr Lache.

'Thorne,' said Splinter. He bowed slightly. 'At your service.'

Dr Lache laughed sharply, unamused. 'Hardly.'

Alone now, without his blockheaded twin brother, Box, or his selfish, deluded younger sister, Chess, Splinter was amidst the Twisted Symmetry and its servants. It was a deadly place to be, for an ordinary mortal, but Splinter had the vision to see that it was also a place of vast possibilities.

The destruction of the Inquisitor, Behrens, had created an opportunity; a Splinter-sized opportunity. However, he would have to be *very* careful; Splinter knew what people would do for the immense power this opportunity promised, and there were others who would want it, others who were better placed than he. This was a lethal game. It was vital *not* to reveal his hand; not yet. His competitors would be stronger than he was: reveal his ambitions too soon and they would wipe him out of existence in a blink. Things didn't get any more lively than this.

But he was Splinter, the King of Rats: smart, mercenary, cunning. He could overcome any obstacle, however deadly, by his ruthless brilliance. And, by solid, meticulous planning.

And Splinter had planned this moment for months.

He had prepared for it with an ascetic devotion. He had lived rough in the woods, had observed the house and its occupants day and night, had given up his cherished old clothes as if parting with a hoard of trusted talismans and he had stolen fresh: a long, scuffed, brown leather trench coat, a black pullover and narrow, blue jeans. He had made himself wear boots. They were black and they felt too long, like boxes on his feet. He had dyed his hair from white to black and tied it in a ponytail to further change his appearance; he had even assumed a new name.

The coat was lined with pockets which he had sewn inside, just as his long-tailed morning coat had been before. The pockets contained his possessions: a box of matches, a knot of string, a pencil, five marbles, a set of lock picks, his switchblade, a bone-handled magnifying glass, a watchmaker's screwdriver, a little wooden box that was actually a portable vortex, a die-sized triangular pyramid and a bottle of black ink which he used to colour his hair where the white showed through.

Day after day, Splinter had explored the ways through the reachings, the narrow pathways that webbed the eternal nothingness of the vortex. He could enter the vortex via the little wooden box that rested within one of the pockets he had sewn inside his long trench coat: a box that he had stolen months ago from the old hag, Ethel, the crackpot commander of that skew-brained, slash-dot, pathetic rabble called the Committee.

There was a logic to the reachings: sometimes. Partly by guesswork, partly by calculation, he could seek out ways that took him to particular places, or moments. But it was painstakingly slow and very dangerous. To be lost in the vortex was to be lost forever; one mistake could cost him eternity. And the reachings had a nasty habit of slipping, from time to time. But, after months of perilous exploration, Splinter's brain contained a perfect map of a network that spread through the vortex to different times and places; a map that he needed if he was to find the *right* time and place.

And now, behind an impassive face, Splinter's brain was busy, assessing, calculating. He knew that at any moment, Dr Lache could kill him, or worse. She had the power.

He should have been dead already. He didn't know she had left the house; something unexpected must have come up; usually she was at home at this time. If she hadn't returned when she did, the buffoon with the gun might have blown his head off. Judging by the way the gun was wobbling, he still might.

Splinter had no idea who had telephoned the doctor, but whoever it was, the call had brought her back just in time. And being just in time, being *here* at *precisely* the right time was a vital part of Splinter's plan.

'Children don't usually break *into* my house,' said Dr Lache, 'although some have tried to escape.' When the boy said nothing, she asked, 'Do you know who I am, Thorne?'

At one end of the sparsely furnished room was a tall glass cabinet containing weights and chains and flywheels. Splinter recognised it as an elaborate variety of grandfather clock. A gentle clicking came from it as time passed.

'I know who you are, Dr Lache,' said Splinter.

'And do you know *what* I am?'

'You are a Crystal Priest,' said Splinter, plainly and then he said, 'A powerful Crystal Priest. But not the *most* powerful.'

He thought he would shatter the huge window as his body was swept from the floor and thrown towards it. But he passed through the glass without sound or impact and then he was hurtling upwards, faster and faster, higher and higher into the night sky. He went so fast that it seemed as if the black clumps of woods and the glistening lake were swooping down, away from him. Rain stung his face and neck and he could barely catch the air to breathe.

Somewhere between the clouds and the lake he stopped, long coat flapping in the gusting air, arms and legs crabbed as if he might stop himself from falling by clinging to the nothingness. The terror of dropping out of the sky was so great that his teeth chattered and his stomach felt as if it were collapsing.

'Is this power enough, Thorne?'

Oriana Lache might have been speaking into his ear, so close and calm was her voice. 'Should we go higher?'

'No, no,' jabbered Splinter, trying to control his juddering jaw, wondering how much time he had.

'Or lower?'

Before he could answer the voice, he was plummeting down feet-first, coat trailing above him. It was just as if his body had been hurled at the water. The glistening blackness rushed at his kicking legs and the whistling air buffeted the breath from him. He tried not to scream. Maybe he would glide through the water like he had through the window.

The lake hit the back of his calves like a hurricane, scooping his legs from under him so fast that his head hit the surface in a smash of spray. Nose, mouth, eyes and ears were filled by the icy rush of water, stinging and blotting out every sense but the desperate need to breathe. His chest ached from the impact and he no longer knew whether he was head up or head down. But he knew he was sinking; not just sinking but being dragged down, or pushed: down so deep that his eardrums felt as if they would implode and his eyeballs burst.

Silt and weed. His fingers closed on the lake bottom and his body came to rest. If he gave in, if he filled his lungs with the deep waters of the lake, he could end this torture.

'Is this power enough, Thorne?'

The voice nuzzled into his ringing, aching ears.

All he needed was a little more time. But he could hold out no longer. He had to breathe.

Again, space collapsed, flinging him up and out of the water and back into the room in Dr Lache's house. Right next to the fire. Too close to the fire.

'You're wet, Thorne,' stated Dr Lache. 'You need to dry out.'

Water coursed from Splinter's sodden hair and clothes as he tried to get up from his hands and knees, in front of the fireplace. But his body wouldn't do what he wanted it to. Instead, he felt himself slipping over the carpet, closer to the snapping flames.

'Maybe we just kill him now?' ventured Boulevant, nervously, as if he could not face what would happen next.

'There's no need to hurry,' explained Oriana Lache, standing and extending her long, graceful fingers towards the fire. 'Go on, Thorne,' she said to Splinter. 'See how hot it is.'

Splinter's face was inches from the nearest flames. The heat was scorching. He thought his eyeballs would boil and the skin curl from his face like burning paper. He tried to see the grandfather clock but his head was held rigid and his eyes were filled with a watery haze.

It *had* to be time.

'How does power feel, Thorne?'

'Release me,' gasped Splinter, sweat bathing his face, the tendons in his neck rigid as cord as he strained to look up, into Dr Lache's eyes. 'Release me or I will have your nexal.'

And then he was sitting on the sofa, behind Dr Lache, his hair and clothes dry, and he was holding the fine chain that Dr Lache always wore about her neck.

The long, graceful fingers pressed against her naked throat, and she gasped, eyes wide.

'Please, no, please,' she begged.

Splinter laughed coldly.

'Shall I use it?' he asked.

'Please, please give it back to me.' Dr Lache was at Splinter's feet, on her knees.

He held the silvery necklace aloft, allowing the fine links to trail over the edges of his hand like beads of water. The pendant with its C and three minute stars swung before the doctor's imploring face.

Splinter leant out of the sofa, the necklace still held high, his face pushed right up to Oriana Lache's.

'Any time I want it,' he whispered, 'I can take it.'

Then he was back on all fours before the fire, the flames almost licking his skin.

'Release me,' he hissed. '*Now.*'

Dr Lache retreated, both hands rubbing at the necklace that was around her throat again. She slumped onto the sofa.

Splinter's body was released and he rolled away. The side of his face was stinging and it was hot to touch, but he wasn't burnt. Swaying slightly, he got to his feet.

'Put the gun down,' he ordered, his ice blue eyes nailed on Dr Lache.

'Please, Boulevant.' Dr Lache swallowed, wresting back her composure. 'Please, put it down.' She looked up at the tall, thin boy in the brown, leather trench coat, still dripping water. Breathing shallowly, she asked, 'How?'

'I can do things,' announced Splinter, too menacing to be boastful. 'Things that you cannot imagine.'

Splinter had known that if he was to survive the coming contest, he would have to make an impression and make it quickly: find a way of securing a foothold amongst his all-powerful competitors. That was why he had spent months picking his way through the vortex: world by world, inch by inch, second by second.

It had taken a mind-crunchingly perfect plotting of the reachings to open up one moment where he could come out of nowhere and snatch Dr Lache's most precious possession before the moment closed and it would be like he had never been there. But he had done it, only days ago. He'd used the vortex to come out of a future moment for no more than ten seconds, and take the necklace by surprise, before vanishing again. So long as Dr Lache didn't happen to check what the immediate future had in store, that moment would be waiting like a flashback. Or was it a flash forward? Either way, he then had to make sure that he was with Dr Lache when that moment happened. The timing had to be perfect. But he had managed it. Just. Breaking into her house to discover that she wasn't there at the precise time he needed her to be there was a disaster. Whoever had phoned to call her back had kept him alive.

Dr Lache was staring up at him, waiting, considering her options maybe. It had taken months of preparation to get to this point. The King of Rats had used all his skill and artifice to steal a blink in time. He would not have such an opportunity again; events were moving too quickly. He had to press home his advantage, at once.

'Any time I want it, I can take it,' repeated Splinter. 'Don't you ever, *ever* forget that.'

'But how?' Dr Lache dared to remove her artistic fingers from the piece of jewellery but she didn't take her eyes off Splinter.

'I have certain skills,' said Splinter. 'And I have knowledge.' Splinter knew all sorts of things. In particular, he knew all sorts of things about the Twisted Symmetry, its methods and its forces. When he had been marooned on Surapoor with that philosopher, pugilist and bug-eyed weirdo, Balthazar Broom, he had studied hard in Balthazar's library. He had lavished weeks upon the Omnicon, the Book of All Things, which could reveal knowledge to anyone clever enough to use it. Balthazar, the fool, had said there were two such incredible books, but one of them was lost.

But Balthazar had been wrong. Splinter had used the fool's Omnicon to discover where its sister volume was kept, a volume that would reveal secrets he desired.

'I know, for example, that the nexal you wear is as precious to you as life.' Splinter raised a hand like an accusing phantom and pointed at Dr Lache's necklace. 'I know that for every Crystal Priest it is their greatest strength,' and now he revealed a smile like the blade of a knife, 'and their greatest weakness.'

Splinter's diligent researches had revealed to him the heart-source of the Twisted Symmetry's most powerful human servants. When a human had distinguished himself or herself by cunning, mercilessness and a fanatical devotion to the Symmetry, it sometimes happened that the Inquisitors would reward them with a gift. The gift might take the shape of a ring, or a bracelet, or a necklace, but always the purpose of this gift, this nexal, was to create a link with the Inquisitors, enabling its human recipient to draw upon the Inquisitors' massive power.

But Splinter saw how clever this was, how beautifully controlling, for what was given could always be taken away. So the Crystal Priests remained forever at the mercy of the Inquisitors.

And Splinter knew that for the time being at least, he was at the mercy of the Crystal Priests. The trick would be to make sure they didn't realise that.

Dr Oriana Lache appeared to have regained her composure. She removed her spectacles, straightened her black dress and crossed one long leg over the other. But Splinter could see that behind the cool hazel eyes, the Crystal Priest's mind was working as deviously as his own.

Rather primly, she said, 'You are an unusual boy, Thorne.'

Splinter did not want her to relax too much. 'Fenley Ravillious is planning to kill you.' Hawk-eyed, he observed the response across the doctor's poised face and body.

'You don't know what you're talking about.'

Her pupils contracted, her voice was working to maintain control; she made every *effort* to appear at ease.

Splinter could smell the fear seep out.

Silently he congratulated himself. It had been a good guess. But then again, it was more than a guess; it was knowledge, knowledge of the things people did for power. Of course the most powerful amongst the Crystal Priests would seek to replace Behrens. But there was space for only him. The competition would have to be destroyed. Splinter understood this; it was useful to him.

'I am a thief,' announced Splinter, surprised by the weightless sensation that came with speaking the truth.

'Boulevant, fetch the boy a mug of cocoa.' Oriana Lache danced her fingers towards the plump factotum who hovered about the fireplace. 'And a towel perhaps? He is dripping.'

'I'll drink nothing, until you see how useful I am to you,' said Splinter, causing Boulevant to stop as if the boy and the Crystal Priest were wresting his puppet strings from one another. 'And don't bother with the towel. It's not my rug I'm dripping on.'

'Maybe you would like a mug of cocoa, doctor?' suggested the short, round man, fingers drumming on the belly of his yellow waistcoat, and an expression of tentative inquiry on his porcine chops.

'Shut up, Boulevant,' snapped Dr Lache. She turned back to Splinter and brushed her damp hair back so that it spread across the top of the sofa.

Splinter felt the room draw darker, the fire yellower and the doctor's eyes grow brighter. Hot, intense, they locked into his.

'Go on, Thorne.' Her lips were pursed, suggesting a smile. Splinter focused on her necklace. Looking into Oriana

Lache's eyes conjured diversions in his thoughts that were unhelpful.

'I am able to move from one place to another, mostly unseen.' He could feel the hot intensity of the doctor's gaze, even if he wasn't looking at her eyes. 'I am able to steal things. Things like your nexal.'

Saying that seemed to break Dr Lache's concentration because one hand rose to her throat and the fear sparked back into her eyes. Whatever thoughts had begun to creep into his mind, Splinter preferred things this way.

You must guard against distractions, warned one of the voices inside his head.

'I can take your nexal any time I want,' hissed Splinter, standing over the doctor. He enjoyed the way her eyes widened and her chest rose and fell sharply as her breathing quickened.

'Please, please, no.'

Splinter's hand was raised above his head as if it might actually swoop down and snatch the necklace. Yellow firelight haloed his tall form. Mouth agape, Boulevant looked from Oriana Lache to Splinter and back to Oriana Lache. His grip tightened on the pistol that dangled by his side.

'Move one millimetre, fat man,' growled Splinter, 'and I'll stuff your guts with your flabby head.' Splinter wasn't sure how he'd do that, but he had been so impressed by General Saxmun Vane's threats of savagery that he was ready to employ a little of the same himself. Splinter was always ready to learn new methods of getting what he wanted and the Commander of the Twisted Symmetry's Dog Troopers had left him in no doubt that the promise of a painful and messy death could focus the mind and promote obedience.

Splinter felt the scar across his left shoulder throb at the thought of the General and how he had slashed him with a mace-blade. The difference between him and the General was that if the General had threatened to stuff Boulevant's head inside Boulevant's stomach, Boulevant would now be blinking gormlessly from inside his own intestines. But Boulevant didn't know Splinter's limitations.

'Drop it,' commanded Splinter.

'Please, drop it,' echoed Dr Lache.

The gun hit the carpet with a dull thud.

Splinter stepped back, smiled, and then lowered his arm, allowing the doctor to see that he could be merciful. But he wanted Dr Lache to see that he could be helpful too.

'Without Fenley Ravillious in the way, you could replace Behrens.'

Oriana Lache leant forwards. 'How do you know these things?'

'Don't worry about that, Dr Lache,' said Splinter, airily, pacing back and forth before the fire, his gait a little uneven. The fool, Broom, had failed to set his ankle properly after it had been fractured by the stonedrakes' marine culverin, on Surapoor. The limp was a constant reminder to him of other people's inadequacies.

'Your problem,' he continued, 'is how to dispose of Ravillious. He is stronger than you, cleverer, if you don't mind me saying so. More powerful.' This time his feet remained on the carpet. Now, Oriana Lache was listening, wanting to hear what he had to say. He paused before the fire, hands clasped behind his back.

'Go on, Thorne.' The doctor slipped her glasses back on and leant forwards, elbows on knees, cupping her neat chin in her hands. Maybe, just maybe she was a little bit impressed, although Splinter decided that he preferred her frightened.

'As I told you, I am a thief.' He paused, purely for dramatic effect. 'If someone were to steal Ravillious's nexal, he would be powerless.'

Splinter didn't need to say more. Dr Lache's eyes glittered, and she fought to restrain the smile that tugged at the corners of her mouth. Her skin was flushed in the tremulous firelight.

'Thorne, you are unlike any boy I have ever met.'

Frightened and impressed. Perfect. Now he had got here, he had to stay in command. But with his one trick played, that wouldn't be easy.

Very smoothly and serious as a schoolmistress, Dr Lache said, 'I must warn you, Thorne, Fenley Ravillious is cunning and cruel and utterly poisonous.'

Quite a lot like you, thought Splinter. But he shrugged indifferently. Show no doubt; show no fear. You are playing against the most ruthless, the most powerful humans to stalk the earth.

Oriana Lache's face tightened with disgust and maybe, thought Splinter, a shade of fear. 'And he is assisted by a creature he calls his daughter.'

'Tethys.' Splinter was displaying a little more of his knowledge, although in truth he knew very little about Ravillious's daughter, save that she was a Crystal Priest, like her father.

'She is different from the rest of us.' Dr Lache began to

wind her hair back onto her head. 'She has her own ... powers.'

Splinter sniffed, as if he didn't want to waste the energy it would take to laugh at Tethys and her mysterious powers.

Dr Lache's hands worked behind her head and her eyes narrowed. 'What you promise to do is so dangerous. Why are you helping me?' Her neat lips pursed and she paused in her coiffure, elbows apart, looking up. 'What do you want in return?'

Splinter smiled, but his icicle eyes were unflinching. 'You have something that I've been looking for.'

CHAPTER 3

The rain had stopped but the velvet darkness of the night tinkled like a celeste as water dripped from the pine trees. Splinter's breath fogged in the thick beam of the torch which wobbled in Boulevant's hands.

'This way,' said Oriana Lache, squelching over the boggy earth in a pair of rubber boots.

'It's cold, isn't it?' ventured Boulevant from the rear. He had left the pistol inside the house. Now that Dr Lache and the boy appeared to have reached an understanding, he punctuated the short walk to the shore of the lake with aimless banter. Splinter ignored him.

Dr Lache stopped by a fringe of reeds. The dark waters stretched ahead of her, glistening like cold oil. Splinter could just discern the trees that ringed the lake, like a black palisade. With a crash of wings and a shriek, an owl broke from the pines to the left, whilst metres ahead snipe volleyed out of the reeds, disturbed by Boulevant's shambling boots. The torch beam swept over the water, cutting through the mist like the sail of a windmill before he steadied it.

'Sorry,' he gasped, regaining his footing.

Dr Lache bowed her head and Splinter began to wonder whether she might turn on him right now. He would be powerless if she did. He said nothing and fought to stop his teeth from chattering as the chill night air seeped through his damp clothes and into his bones.

At first it sounded as if the water had begun to drip from the trees more rapidly, but the tinkling noise grew more intense and became the sound of a million glass balls rolling and clashing against one another. A stone's throw from where Oriana Lache stood, head bowed, the dark waters surged and then began to rise. Louder and louder, there came a creaking and snapping and ringing: a sound Splinter had never heard before but which he could only think of as the opposite of glass smashing. Maybe it was the sound of glass being squeezed. As the squealing chimes rang in the darkness, the nearest stretch of the lake elevated to a point like the apex of a pavilion, the waters not so much rolling away as hardening and becoming part of the growing structure.

Then there was silence, apart from the slap of the lake water about the low, crystal roof that pitched up from the ground, immediately before them. Torchlight glanced off it, revealing a surface like a vast, rough-cut diamond.

'Spin symmetry.' Dr Lache spoke softly.

'I thought they were Twisted,' observed Splinter.

'No, Thorne, *this* is spin symmetry.' Dr Lache pointed at the construction which glinted in the darkness. 'The particles constituting the chamber can rotate through half, full or double turns. At half spin the chamber is revealed, but if they turn through two revolutions, the matrix is rearranged so that it merges with the lake, actually becomes part of the lake again.' She looked at Splinter even though the night masked her face. 'It is the most perfect concealment, hiding the identity of one thing by transforming it into something else.'

Splinter sniffed to indicate that it would take more than spin symmetry to impress him.

'Boulevant, torch,' ordered Oriana Lache in clipped tones.

'Coming. I'm coming,' blustered Boulevant, splashing through the reed bed.

'Who *is* he?' Splinter whispered to Dr Lache, wondering why one of the elect should be saddled with such a buffoon.

'A lover's child.' Oriana Lache spoke with quiet precision.

Splinter was wondering at that when a hand snatched the back of his trench coat.

Boulevant whooped and cursed as he banana-skinned into the bog, heaving Splinter with him. There was an eruption of peaty water, Splinter felt a jet of mud spatter his face and the torch was snuffed face-down in the mire.

'Sorry, sorry, sorry,' babbled Boulevant, slapping about on hands and knees. It sounded as if someone was thrashing the earth with a limp fish.

'This way,' said Oriana Lache, paying no attention to the tangle of bodies and walking towards the glinting roof.

Boulevant grunted as the flat of Splinter's boot crashed into his cheek.

'Watch your step, fat man,' hissed Splinter, 'if you want me to watch mine.'

Boulevant keeled onto his side with a splash. 'Sorry,' he burbled, finding the torch at last.

Splinter followed Dr Lache's silhouette, down a steep flight of stone steps and into a deep chamber suffused with a wan, violet light. The high walls were octagonal, crystal like the canopied roof most of the way round but stone where the lake bank was.

'It's like being under water,' mused Splinter, who not so long ago had experienced the bottom of the lake without the benefit of air.

'It is,' agreed Dr Lache. She turned on the spot, indicating the transparent boundaries of the chamber beyond which there pressed the night-filled waters of the lake. 'These are not so much walls as the water transformed.'

Splinter revolved similarly and could not see what they had come for. The chamber was empty.

Boulevant squelched down the last of the steps, check trousers filthy and yellow waistcoat polka-dotted with mud. His mac was smeared with peat. He clicked off the torch, sat down and grinned as he ran a grimy hand through his receding, grey curly hair.

'Never knew this was here!' he exclaimed. A livid graze on his cheek marked Splinter's boot-strike.

'I haven't been here for over sixty years,' muttered Oriana Lache. 'I have had no particular need.'

Splinter was unsurprised by Dr Lache's youthful body. It belonged to the Symmetry; of course it had defeated age. But his mind was fixed on something else.

'Where is it?' he demanded.

'All about us,' replied the doctor.

Splinter fixed her with a chill glare. 'It is no use to *me* if it is all about us, Dr Lache.'

The doctor swallowed and nodded. She raised her fine face and opened a palm as if catching a falling apple, then drew it downwards, closing her fingers into a fist.

Splinter heard the air whisper and thought he saw dust storming about them before it rushed in from every direction, gathering above Dr Lache's fist. Piece by piece, as if filling the space by segments, a book appeared: folio-sized, cumbersome, suspended in the air at chest height.

'Spin symmetry?' asked Splinter, testing out this new piece of knowledge.

'No.' Dr Lache stepped back from the thick volume which hung before them at an angle perfect for reading. 'Particle-grid superimposition. The subatomic structure of the book has been mapped onto the subatomic structure of the chamber.' She shrugged. 'All I had to do was re-plot the trillions of coordinates to pull the book together.'

'*This* is what I call security,' approved Splinter, recalling the locked, metal case that the fool, Broom, had relied upon: a locked, metal case that was no barrier to Splinter's lock picks and clever fingers. Then, being careful not to appear overly-impressed by the doctor, he said, 'The Inquisitors re-plotted the book. All you did, Dr Lache, was to rely upon that nexal you wear.' And when he jibed her like that, the doctor cast her hazel eyes towards the beaten floor.

'Go now. Both of you.' Splinter dismissed Oriana Lache and Boulevant with a wave of his hand.

'But ...' began Dr Lache.

'But nothing.' Splinter stabbed a finger in her direction. 'I have been generous with you already. Don't test me, doctor.'

'Please, Thorne.' Oriana Lache held up her palms, beseechingly. 'Don't misunderstand. I only wanted to stay, to help.'

'Go,' snapped Splinter. 'It is *you* who needs *my* help. I need nothing.' He turned his back on the doctor, knowing there was nothing he could do to protect it. But he heard two pairs of footsteps ascending the stairwell and then he was alone.

'The Omnicon,' whispered Splinter, approaching the volume. 'The Book of All Things.' How clever of him to have used Balthazar's Omnicon to locate the second. He sighed in a long, low hiss as he acknowledged his brilliance in this matter. Now he had to use that brilliance to plumb the secrets of the book. Having lavished days upon Balthazar's copy, he was adept in its use: how to flick between the two pages it contained, finding the clues on one page that led him closer to what he wanted to discover on the second, and repeating the process, moving back and forth between the pages until, eventually, he found the piece of knowledge he sought.

The book was waiting for him. It wanted to be read. It wanted to help the King of Rats. Splinter remembered this feeling too: the pull of the Omnicon, his desire to use it and its desire to be used. This was the way of warp technology, the processes and instruments designed by the warps, the Twisted Symmetry's scientists. It called you, it gave itself to you, it awoke appetites and sensations that you didn't know you had. Splinter enjoyed these feelings

But before his fingers alighted on the covers, they reached for one of the pockets inside his long, scuffed, muddy trench coat. They closed on the die-sized, triangular pyramid.

Splinter had found this miniature pyramid when rooting through the crates in Balthazar's cave on Surapoor and with the instinct of a street rat who lived by his wits and his fingertips, he had known at once that it would be something valuable. Something special.

He sat it on the palm of his hand. Its plain, metal surfaces were cold. With his other hand he opened the sturdy front cover of the Omnicon. A pale glow seeped from the ivory-coloured page, creating a distinct aura within the violet light of the lake chamber. Splinter leant over the page and his thin, pale face turned white, although his dyed hair remained black. His eyes were bright.

He began to flip between the two pages, their contents changing as his mind moved between the clues he found and the Omnicon responded to his thoughts.

MATTER – SHAPE – PYRAMIDS

At PYRAMIDS, the page flooded the room with holograms, throwing out a variety of figures, different in pitch and size. Splinter walked amongst them, studying them, considering which most closely resembled the tiny pyramid he held.

Splinter and the Omnicon working together. A perfect meeting of mind and warp technology.

When he saw a small, plain, triangular pyramid, he returned his thoughts to the page and began to narrow down the alternatives that the following pages presented to him. By the time he found what he wanted, a pearl glow was leaking into the surrounding waters of the lake and the violet light of the chamber seemed correspondingly dimmer. The canopied roof had tuned from black to grey. But although his eyes were sore from lack of sleep, Splinter was too excited to be tired.

He had switched the display from hologram to diagram; Splinter had learnt that once he had tracked down the desired information, the book would present the information in the form he wished.

He tilted the book flat and placed the little pyramid on the glowing page, measuring it against the diagram as he had done with more than a hundred diagrams already. But this time, when the annotations instructed him to strike the pyramid with metal, and he tapped it with the watchmaker's screwdriver, the high, singing note matched the pitch and tone of the note emitted by the Omnicon perfectly.

This was the pyramid he had been searching for.

Splinter pocketed the pyramid and inspected the diagram. Dimensions, tangents, quadrants and perspectives were marked upon it in minute detail, the arrows and labels cutting across the miniscule text in a complex notation of technicalities. There were words he didn't recognise and text that his tired eyes simply couldn't read.

Sitting cross-legged, underneath the Book of All Things, Splinter rubbed his aching calves and hamstrings and stretched his neck. How long had he been standing here, poring over the extraordinary volume? Too long; his eyes were too weary to decipher the dense text now.

'Explain,' he thought. 'Just the basics. Enough to know what it is. What it does.'

And, obligingly, the Omnicon responded so that Splinter heard his own voice speaking inside his own head.

'The Hermetic Codex. Constructed by Hermes Trismegistus over five thousand years ago. Employing a primitive form of dimensional trigonometry, it will display up to three termination points for any given life.'

Splinter interrupted the voice. 'What's dimensional trigonometry?'

'Bringing different times and places together at *one* time and place,' replied the book in his own voice. 'Like a parallax bangle.'

'Don't know what one of those is,' complained Splinter. 'What's a termination point?'

'A possible death,' came the answer. 'Or, to be precise, the moments just before that death.'

It will let me see how I might die, realised Splinter. But these were only *possible* deaths. So ... with a jolt he understood that the deaths were only *possible* deaths because by seeing them, or at least the moments that led up to them, he could avoid them.

To know where death lay in wait; in his current circumstances that could be very, *very* useful. Splinter licked his lips and returned to the book. 'How do I use it?'

'The user's blood will catalyze the Codex and make it specific to the user. However, it is recommended that the device is not used.'

'Not used!' echoed Splinter in dismay.

'Under Time-Space Regulation one-zero-four-eight, use of an Hermetic Codex is proscribed without authority from CASRA [see footnote 5].'

'Wait!' Splinter held up a hand even though to the best of his knowledge the Omnicon didn't have eyes to see it. He

-[42]-

breathed slowly in an effort to be patient. 'What does footnote 5 say?'

The book quoted back. 'CASRA (The Cosmological Agency for Statutes, Records and Artefacts), also known as *the Sages* or *the Time Historians*, is the pan-dimensional, multiversal authority responsible for monitoring the Time Spiral. It holds the records of all continuum events, measures node periods and regulates temporal interference. It is a politically neutral body, incorporated into all wave-particle realities at a cosmic scale and therefore immune to all events, with the exception of total multiversal destruction.'

'In other words, it's the people who make the rules,' observed Splinter, critically. 'So even the universes are organised by people who make rules?' He sniffed. In Splinter's ideal universe, only one person would make the rules: him. 'Go on then,' he snapped at the book. 'Why won't they let me use the Codex without permission?'

'The old technology is unpredictable and its use may be damaging to health, to the extent that it may initiate the event it is designed to avoid.'

'Brilliant,' grumbled Splinter aloud. 'So using it might kill me. And that's if I get permission from the cosmic crashers in the first place.' Which, he realised, accounted for why that great fool, Balthazar Broom, had left the tiny pyramid in the bottom of the crate rather than use it himself. However great a fool he was, Balthazar Broom hadn't been foolish enough to experiment with the Hermetic Codex.

Splinter yawned. There were other matters to delve into, secrets to unravel, but not now. Now he was too tired.

He stood and slammed shut the Omnicon. Brooding, he marched up the stone steps and out of the chamber. When death came stalking, he would have to defeat it without the aid of the Codex.

CHAPTER 4

Every morning they took breakfast on the decked balcony
that spanned the front of Dr Lache's house. The house was
built where the ground began to rise above the lake, so that
the view was over the sage and dun reed beds, across the
silver waters and out to the pines which ran smooth in every
direction, ruffling like fur when the wind blew. It was hard
to believe that the clatter and stink of the city was only a
short drive away. But, considered Splinter as he ripped the
tip off another croissant, this was what you could do if you
had grease; and the backing of the Twisted Symmetry, the
most powerful organisation in the universes.

A small, wrought-iron table sat between Splinter and
Oriana Lache, its circular top and rococo metalwork painted
white. On it was spread breakfast: juice, pastries, butter and
two sorts of jam. Splinter lifted a tall glass of sweetened
lemon to his lips, squinting over the rim as the late-spring
sun cast a net of sparkles over the dimpled surface of the
lake. How different from breakfast at the wharf, where he
had lived with his gang of street rats before the hunters had
come and smashed it up. Not that breakfast at the wharf had

ever been a regular event. And the only water to admire had been the stewing eddies of the river as it slipped between the clanking factory sector and the disgusting effluence of the Pit.

He gulped the juice and his leather trench coat creaked slightly as he sat back, legs outstretched. Splinter, in contemplative mood.

In some respects, things were working out nicely. But only in *some* respects.

'Are your researches proceeding satisfactorily?' asked Dr Lache, so measured, so precise, that Splinter knew immediately that she was probing him. She wore a coral, cashmere coat over her black dress and her porcelain face would have been doll-like but for the severe, horn-rimmed spectacles and her sharply arching eyebrows. The nexal looked fragile about her delicate throat.

Splinter switched his gaze from Dr Lache to the margin of the lake where the chamber containing the Omnicon was located. At the moment, all that could be seen was water. 'Satisfactorily,' he sniffed. But that was not entirely true.

He had been with Dr Lache and Boulevant for nearly three weeks. Most nights he had spent alone within the transformed waters of the lake, the doctor dismissed after she had reconstructed the aquatic chamber. Bathed in the aura of the Book of All Things, he had immersed himself in a study of the Crystal Priests, and Fenley Ravillious in particular. He had discovered the approximate location of Ravillious's house; somewhere within the Wreckage, the industrial wastelands to the south of the megalopolis. But he had felt his brow prickle with sweat when the Omnicon refused to divulge any more secrets about the strange dwelling.

Oriana Lache expected him to be able to penetrate Ravillious's lair; she believed Splinter had amazing powers of his own. If he didn't tackle Ravillious soon, her belief in these special powers would vanish, with fatal consequences for him. He had to deliver, without further delay, but that was going to be difficult. He would have to find a way into a house that was cloaked in a secrecy that not even the Omnicon could penetrate. And then, he would have to deal with Ravillious himself.

But there had been more than Fenley Ravillious to consider: much more. Splinter had been greatly occupied in learning all that he could about the Inquisitors, their powers and, most importantly, how they came to power. But during these researches he was pricked by this question: was he directing the book, or was the book directing him?

The Omnicon introduced him to ideas he had never sought and put before his eyes images he would never have conceived of, unaided. It liked to show him power; who had it and what it could do. With the assistance of the Omnicon, Splinter had spent many nights absorbed in the company of kings. They spoke with him, gave him advice, wisdom. Some even admired his ruthless brilliance. The kings of the earth consulting with the King of Rats! This was intoxicating stuff, yet Splinter kept a grip on his ambitions and focused on the practicalities.

But gnawing at him more persistently than the mysteries of Ravillious's lair, more hungrily than the promise of power, was the matter of the blank page.

Balthazar Broom had said that the Omnicon revealed only facts; he had said that it would not reveal the future. But that had not stopped Splinter from trying. And when he had consulted the book about Chess, or Box, when he sought to divine what the future held for them, it offered him nothing, no chain of references to follow. But when he performed this exercise upon himself, the Omnicon led him on every occasion to a blank page. He could not understand why the Book of All Things would lead him to this page when it refused to respond in this way for anyone else.

He had no idea what the blank page meant, but it worried him. It nagged at him. He suspected it was not a good sign.

'You look tired,' observed Oriana, and Splinter wondered whether there was actually a hint of genuine concern in her voice.

'I know.' He had seen the dark rings around his eyes in his bedroom mirror.

'I thought I saw you this morning, walking on the far side of the lake.' Oriana Lache jutted her small chin in the direction she meant.

Splinter gave a grunt which meant that it wasn't him.

'I know. It was too tall anyway.'

'Couldn't you see, with all this power of yours? Couldn't you telescope your vision or something like that?'

Dr Lache pursed her lips. 'I tried.'

Which meant that the figure had managed, somehow, to evade her observations. Splinter wished now that he had said it *was* him, just to keep the doctor on her toes.

'Doesn't that worry you?' he asked. 'That whoever it was could hide from you?'

Dr Lache smiled at Splinter. 'Why should I worry, Thorne? I have you to protect me.'

Splinter's white face reddened. He wondered whether she was jesting. He changed the subject. 'Have you got a cat?' he asked.

'No.' One of Dr Lache's arched eyebrows arched even further. 'Why on earth do you ask that?' She gave a little laugh.

'No reason,' replied Splinter, who always had a reason for the things he asked.

Dr Lache never went to the small pantry, next to the operating theatre-sized kitchen. Splinter had located it on his first day at the house, having explored the open-plan, split levels with their big views of the lake and the pine woods, in a matter of minutes. The house was full of valuable items, paintings, figurines, rugs, but none of them were what Splinter would have classified as 'liftable': not without a truck. However, the pantry was a different matter. To a street rat who had lived with the devious ache of hunger for most of his life, an unguarded supply of food was irresistible.

The pantry was really a walk-in cupboard, but it had its own light which meant that Splinter could shut himself away and sample all the delicacies within: caviar, quails' eggs, Parma ham, chocolate truffles, spoonfuls of pâté de foie gras. What the Omnicon delivered to his mind, Dr Lache's pantry delivered to his belly.

However, two mornings ago, he had seen something that had staunched his enduring hunger and made the bile rise in his throat. On the floor, just inside the doorway, he had found a frothy little puddle, lime in colour and ringed by a yellowish foam. It had looked like cat sick, except that within the sticky fluid he had noticed what appeared at first to be little stones. Squatting down and on closer inspection, Splinter had seen that these were not stones. They were teeth: human teeth.

The acrid stench had made him gag and sent him loping from the kitchen. How did human teeth end up in cat sick on Dr Lache's pantry floor? Splinter had mulled this over as he had lain on his canopied bed in the guest room, with the blinds down, hoping to sleep after a long night with the Omnicon. But sleep hadn't come and when, eventually, curiosity had driven him back to the pantry, the puddle and teeth had gone and the floor was clean.

'Boulevant has been acting strangely. Have you noticed?' Dr Lache gazed into the middle distance. From the woods beyond the lake there came the whine of an engine.

Splinter *had* noticed. He had noticed a surly air, a new tendency to silence, an aptitude for appearing about the house unexpectedly, but he had been too immersed in his researches to give Boulevant's novel habits any further consideration.

A jeep emerged from the screen of trees on the far shore of the lake, canoes lashed to its roof. The occupants climbed out. Splinter could see two adults and a child: a young child to judge by the squealing laughter that drifted across to them.

'There should be no boating on this lake.' Dr Lache frowned. 'It is against the rules.'

'How wicked,' said Splinter, 'to break rules.'

With a rattle of china, Boulevant appeared at the end of

the balcony bearing a tray balanced with cups and saucers, a jug of milk and a steaming cafetière.

Oriana Lache slid her eyes away from where the canoes were splashing into the water's edge and towards the approaching Boulevant. Splinter saw how minutely she observed him. He stomped towards them with a total disregard for her scrutiny.

'Won't you join us?' suggested Dr Lache as the tray was clattered down. 'I am planning a little entertainment,' and her hazel eyes flitted towards the family entering the cold waters of the lake: an adult in one canoe and an adult and child in the other, yellow life-jackets bright against the dark reflections of the trees.

'No,' came the abrupt response.

'Do you have a cat?' Splinter asked him. He recalled seeing Boulevant lurking outside the kitchen when he had first come upon the puddle of tooth-filled sick.

'Thorne must want a cat.' There was a trill of amusement in Dr Lache's voice.

'Nine lives. Very useful,' observed Boulevant. When Dr Lache bent forward to sniff the coffee steam he said, 'I've tried it already.'

'We cannot be too careful.' Dr Lache sniffed.

'Careful of what?' asked Splinter, curious.

Oriana Lache folded her hands in her lap and looked out at the lake. 'When will you be ready to deal with Ravillious?'

Splinter had sensed that this question was coming. This was what Dr Lache had been waiting to ask. He caught the distant splash of the paddles and the beat of the deepening water on the canoe shells. 'In a couple more days.' Firmly, he added, 'I have been reconnoitring his house. I am close now.'

'It is no ordinary house,' warned Dr Lache.

Splinter shrugged. 'I am no ordinary thief.' It was vital not to reveal uncertainty, weakness. He guessed that already, Dr Lache was wondering whether he could really do what he had promised. If she doubted him, she might decide to test his powers for herself. That would go badly for Splinter.

'You've hurt yourself,' she said to Boulevant.

Boulevant looked at the narrow bandage wrapped around his middle finger. 'A cut. That's all.'

'Are you well?' Dr Lache's concern appeared genuine. 'You seem out of colour.'

'I am very well,' replied Boulevant, who marched away.

'I prefer him like this,' said Splinter. Then he noticed a change in Dr Lache's breathing: it had become shallow, more rapid. When he looked at her, her eyes were closed.

'A boy,' she murmured, moistening her lips. 'Seven or eight years old. I hear his heart. Their hearts beat so quickly, little children.' She smiled to herself. 'He's leaning out, touching the water. Do you see how he wants the water?'

She was right, even though her eyes were closed. Splinter could see the small figure stretching over the edge of the canoe.

'Little boys take such big risks,' muttered Dr Lache.

You're telling me, thought Splinter.

'Perhaps we might continue to work together, once you have brought me Ravillious's nexal,' she mused.

Splinter couldn't tell whether it was that, or what she was experiencing from across the water which spread a flush across her face. Her eyes remained shut, her breathing snatched and now the finger of her left hand moved minutely.

'What are you doing?'

'One ... two ... three ... four straps ... all undone.' The same wistful smile, eyes shut. 'And the life-jacket is too big for him. Of course, his parents have noticed nothing.'

A peal of laughter from the canoes. Splinter watched, transfixed.

'They drown so quickly, little children.' Oriana was hoarse with excitement. 'But *how* they struggle.'

She blew gently and on the far side of the lake, a wave rose up and nudged the canoe. If the little boy hadn't been leaning out, the canoe wouldn't have capsized. But his small body, extending over the side, was just enough to tip it.

The splash wasn't great, but the screaming and yelling was instant.

Splinter saw the tiny head slip through the neck of the open life-jacket and vanish beneath the water before appearing for a moment and then slipping into the lake again.

Dr Lache's eyes opened wide, glazed with pleasure. 'You feel his terror?' She inhaled, sucking in the fear, the energy. 'Do you *feel* it?'

'Yes ... yes,' stuttered Splinter. 'I feel it.' He looked at her, seeing how the delight crept beneath her skin, and he realised that whatever he felt, it was not the same as Oriana Lache.

'It's dark in the water. And cold. Stay down. Stay down.' She breathed slowly, heavily.

'They've got him,' gasped Splinter, seeing one of the adults tugging a limp body to the shallows. Then he saw Oriana Lache staring at him.

'Can you handle this, Thorne? Are you able to join us?'

There was no time for doubt. 'I hope he dies,' he lied.

Oriana Lache smiled. 'No need to hope, Thorne. The child is dead already. Leave hope for its parents.' She stood. 'I have a meeting. The CREX Corporation is funding a new public hospital and I have the pleasure of opening it. When I return, I want you to tell me exactly when you will be calling upon Fenley Ravillious.'

Her heels clipped on the planks and then she had gone, leaving only a whisper of perfume.

Splinter spent a long time looking across the lake. He watched the kneeling parents, saw the ambulance come jolting out of the trees, knew what lay underneath the blanket that covered the stretcher, saw the vehicles depart and then he felt the trees reclaim their silence.

He poured some coffee and the cold, viscous fluid dribbled into the cup, unappetisingly. He held out the saucer and watched his hand. No wobbles.

'Good,' he said to himself. 'You know that this will get messy. You know it will get lively. Weakness is death.'

But the coffee was too bitter to drink and even though he was surrounded by utter tranquillity, he couldn't blot out the sound of sobbing.

Somebody had entered the bedroom.

Raw with sleep, Splinter's eyes bulged in the black fog of night.

He had gone to bed early. Oriana Lache had not returned from her engagement so the lake chamber had not been opened for him and after a day of listless wandering about the house, the fatigue of so many nights buried in the glamour of the Omnicon had rushed through his body like a fever. Bed curtains drawn, he had collapsed on the high mattress, fully clothed.

But now, he was not alone.

He had caught the scuff of a foot on the other side of the bed curtains. Just the one. But one was all it took to wake the King of Rats.

Who was it? Who was slipping through the darkness, coming closer to the bed?

Splinter tasted the air. No scent. So it wasn't the doctor.

Boulevant then? Boulevant was dumpy and clumsy. Boulevant didn't move stealthy as a cat.

Silence.

Splinter knew that whoever was out there had realised that he was listening. A thief could sense things like that.

Or an assassin.

Body rigid, he allowed his right hand to creep across his ribs and into a chest pocket. His fingers closed on the cold handle of the switchblade and he drew it out, smoothly as a surgeon. He breathed deeply, drawing in oxygen for the explosion that was about to follow. Muffling the knife within the blankets, he released the blade. Then he closed his eyes, tried to gauge where the visitor was moving and calculated whether to attack first or wait.

To his left, inches from his head, the bed curtain stirred the air. He thought he heard breathing.

Now.

The blade ripped through the curtain, ramming home, burying itself where Splinter had guessed the interloper's face would be. But it pierced only air and Splinter had to grasp the velvet drape to stop himself toppling off the bed.

He had been tricked.

Behind me, he realised, an instant before his spine nearly snapped from the blow to his lower back.

The floor came at him out of the darkness and he tasted split lip. His knife thudded out of reach. Silver dots speckling the edge of his vision, he felt fingers close over his windpipe and now the darkness burst red.

Splinter's hands dived into his coat, chasing through the pockets. He tried to roll and throw off his assailant who wasn't heavy. But he was pinned to the floor as if he had been staked there. As the air was choked from him, his mind shrank to a single purpose.

The box of matches was free. His left hand pulled lamely at the stranger's grip but his right worked to extract one match and push it into the striking surface of the box.

His eyes were bursting with sprays of colour so he barely saw the flare. But as the box burst into flame, he felt the heat. He shoved the flaming box up and into the face of his attacker.

There was a crackle and the rank smell of burning hair and for an instant, Splinter saw dark eyes in a taut, white face and then he was free. He dropped the burning box and rolled away, fingers throbbing with dog-bite pain.

Near the bed, the figure was etched yellow as fire haloed its head. Splinter heard it hiss but in rage or pain, he couldn't tell. He scrambled to his knees and pitched himself in the direction of the open door. But as soon as he began to run, his legs were pulled from under him and he slammed onto the floor. Then he was sliding back, towards the bed, dragged by nothing that he could see or feel.

His boots were met by a length of bed curtain that wrapped itself up his limbs like a snake. Then the fabric burst alight, fire swallowing his legs up to his thighs.

'You want fire?' hissed the figure, slapping the flames away from its own head with its hands, but maintaining its invisible hold over Splinter's legs.

'No,' yelled Splinter, legs trapped within the flaming coils.

What happened next happened very quickly.

Somebody else entered the bedroom and the door slammed shut.

The assassin backed away, head still streaming fire, and ran for the window, leaping through the glass and into the night with a crash. Splinter was hauled up from the floor and slung across the shoulders of whoever had just entered the room. Coils of flaming curtain still burning around his legs, he was carried through the shattered window and then he was thrown onto the marshy ground.

Spluttering in a bed of reeds, Splinter was able to writhe until the sodden earth had extinguished the flames that had been eating around his legs. He lay there, panting, and the cool, damp darkness swallowed him. He heard the silence and knew he was alone.

He buried his burnt right hand in the silt, letting the throb dissolve into the clammy mud and he kicked the charred shreds of curtain from his legs. Eyes closed, he drank lungfuls of damp air and as he listened to an owl screeching, he realised two things.

First, there had been two strangers at Dr Lache's house: the one who had come to murder him and the one who had saved him. And second, his situation was more dangerous than he had appreciated. Death was stalking him from more than one direction. So he had no alternative; whatever the risks, he would have to use the Hermetic Codex.

CHAPTER 5

Chess could taste the mist, ice-cold, floating off the unseen river. It drifted over the rubble, gathered in thick swirls at the foot of the ruined walls, draped the wharf in silence. Nobody else was awake, but these days she hardly slept. Snores and the somnial shufflings of the street rats were all that disturbed the breaking light.

She sensed too much. That was how it felt. Every fall of stone dust, every lick of wind, every smell pressed so far into her mind that the inside of her head became a replica of everything that was outside. Except that she was starting to change things. In the replica world inside her head, Chess could see and hear things that other people couldn't see or hear outside: shadows, voices, cracks in the apparently solid screen of the world around her. And when she let her mind swim up to the cracks, take a look at what was on the other side, there were shapes, sometimes, and great shifting seas of colour or sound, chasms filled with light or darkness, or an aching nothingness.

Chess sighed and blew at a coil of mist which rolled over her upturned face. This was how things were when you began to shift between the dimensions, when you had allowed your body to slip between the spaces within space. It was as if the moorings that were meant to fasten you to your own world became loose. Unless you kept an eye on yourself, it was easy to slip out of the time and place you were meant to be in.

'Chess.'

This wasn't the first time that Chess had heard the voice.

'Chess.'

Nobody else had heard it. She could tell that because nobody else had stirred. The slow rhythm of hundreds of sleepers was unbroken, their slack, curiously flat forms immobile and shrouded in mist within the ramshackle honeycomb of plywood and polythene that lined the high, broken walls of the warehouses.

'Chess.'

It wasn't her imagination. It was a real voice, quite gentle, but definite. Probably a man's, although she couldn't be sure. It was coming from where the debris of the wharf was sluiced by the passing river.

Chess kicked off the thin blanket. She had been lying in her jeans, jumper and leather jacket. She pushed her feet into her trainers but didn't bother with the laces. Clawing the knots from her thick chestnut hair, she shambled into the mist.

She had not expected the head.

There wasn't any blood. It must have been drained of blood before it had been skewered on the iron pole. The pole had been driven into the smashed bricks, a metre from the scum-frothed shallows. The head was at the same height as her own. When she had last seen it, it had been attached to the rest of the Bank; the Bank, who had been so hungry to ransack the profits of the CREX Corporation, who had ordered Chess and Pacer and Anna to steal the data for him when they had broken into the CREX tower at the Cones. Once inside the tower, they had destroyed the cerebral torus, the Twisted Symmetry's computer brain. That had put an end to the Twisted Symmetry's child-stealing, and they had got the Bank his data which, it was now clear, had put an end to the Bank. You couldn't steal from the Twisted Symmetry and expect to live.

Chess breathed slowly and realised that she wasn't frightened by what she was looking at. She had seen so many horrible things. A head on a stick could not compete with what she had witnessed in the Twisted Symmetry's scream rooms. What she felt was pity: pity for the Bank. She hoped they had killed him quickly. At least they had left him his spectacles, although one lens was smashed.

The eyes in the bald, bull-head opened and the corpse-purple lips moved. 'Chess.'

'What?' Chess stuck her fists in the pockets of her leather jacket.

Silence.

'If this was meant to frighten me, it hasn't.'

The Bank's jowls wobbled and a hiss of laughter issued from the decapitated head. 'What has happened to Chess Tuesday?'

'She's grown up.'

Which was true. She guessed she must be nearly fourteen by now. She could do what she wanted. She could walk away from the head, if she wanted. Except that she didn't want to walk away. And with that, she felt the first shiver of fear. This was the enemy, talking to her, and she wanted to listen. That was what made them so dangerous.

'We must apologise for our choice of mouthpiece, Chess. But since you destroyed our brother with such ease, we dare not come too close.'

Destroying the Inquisitor, Behrens, had *not* been easy. It had cost her her right hand although the Committee had given her a new one. And it had nearly cost her her mind. The voice was mocking her, gently, although she knew that the Twisted Symmetry were frightened of what she could do, what she was capable of, even if she didn't understand this herself.

So she was frightened of them, and they were frightened of her. What drove her on was her desire to find Splinter and her desire to find the Eternal, the weapon that the Twisted Symmetry wanted her to use to end time. She wanted to find it, and destroy it.

'We don't want to fight you, Chess. We don't want to fight anyone.'

The voice sounded so reasonable. Chess swallowed hard. This was what the Inquisitors did: they made you question what you thought you knew. If she was going to listen, she would have to be very, very careful. She would have to guard her ears. After months of hunting her, trying to take her by force, the Twisted Symmetry had been held at bay by Julius and the Blood Sentinels. But Chess remembered what Julius had said: Julius, the commander of the Blood Sentinels, half-man, half-god, whose blood had been mixed with hers to save her from herself.

They will work from within. And that is when the Inquisitors are most powerful.

'Do you know what we want? Really?'

'You want to destroy everything so that *you* can live forever.' But when Chess heard her own voice it sounded unconvincing, as if she was just reciting a childish taunt that somebody else had taught her. And, immediately, the enemy used her own thoughts against her.

'Chess, please,' sighed the voice. 'For once in your life think for *yourself*.' Another weary sigh. 'We want peace. Eternal peace, for everyone.'

Which was true, in a way, if nothingness was the same thing as peace, if destroying the multiverse and everything in it was peace, if prolonging the Inquisitors' own existence at the cost of eternity was peace.

'Aren't you tired, Chess? Tired of all of this?'

They were using her against herself, Chess knew that. She *was* tired. Desperately tired. She held back the ocean of exhaustion which made her limbs ache, her head throb, her eyes raw, which threatened to drown her if she gave in.

'We are tired. Just like you. If you only helped us, Chess, there would be no more tiredness, no more suffering. It would all stop. How can it be wrong for you to help us to stop the suffering?'

'I won't help you.' Chess wanted to sound defiant but she heard her own voice and it sounded merely sulky.

'We're not going to leave you, Chess. We understand how you have been poisoned against us. This will take time, but we are patient.' The eyes startled her by blinking and rolling to the left, looking over her shoulder. Then she heard a foot scrape on brick. Someone was approaching.

'Answer this: who offers an eternity of suffering and *who* offers an eternity of rest?' The eyes blinked twice and shut but the voice said, 'All we ask is that you think for yourself. Don't let them use you, Chess. Don't let the Committee betray you. Again.'

And then the head said no more, but a small street rat who had come out of the mist to see who had been talking by the river began to scream and she kept on screaming until two of the bigger rats had heaved the pole out of the ground and hurled pole and head into the dark waters of the river.

Screaming. The little girl was still screaming and Chess could see the Bank's bespectacled head blinking at her on its pole.

The screaming became a shrill shriek of tyres.

'Chess!'

Pacer grabbed Chess's arm, yanking her out of the road. The Bank's glasses became flashing headlights and the car swerved and screamed past them.

'Wake up!' Pacer shouted at her. 'It's like you're not here. What's wrong with you?'

'Nothing's wrong,' groused Chess, marching down the pavement, heading for the college gates. Pacer stamped after her, his dark face hidden within the hood of his black combat jacket.

'You keep acting like some slash-dot bonehead. Can't you act normal?'

'I was thinking about the Bank,' muttered Chess, staring at the pavement to avoid having to look at anyone who passed by. 'About his head.'

'Still?' Exasperated, Pacer grabbed her right arm and hauled her round to face him. 'Chess, that was months ago.'

'OK. I know. But it never stops. Wherever I go, *they* talk to me. Heads, everywhere. Statues, adverts, video screens, dolls. All the time.'

In some people this might have been a sign of madness, but Pacer knew that the Twisted Symmetry were real; he knew that the world wasn't always as it looked and he knew that over the past few months, inch by inch, Chess was being drawn closer and closer to breaking point.

'You're not on your own, you know.' He relaxed his grip and slid his arm up hers to squeeze her shoulder.

Chess nodded, biting her lip. 'I've been working on shifting.'

'I know.' Pacer looked at her carefully from inside his hood.

'I'm getting better at it,' continued Chess, automatically stepping into the gutter as two jack students barged past without apology, laughing with each other as if Chess wasn't there. 'I can shift my whole body in and out of space now. I can get into the vortex just by thinking about it. I can slow time for up to twenty minutes; at least that's what Anna said when she timed it.'

'Nice one.' Pacer spat thoughtfully, wondering how Anna timed twenty minutes that were going slow. Then, turning to useful practicalities he added, 'If you was robbing you could get away better. The crashers would always be late.'

An awkward pause. 'I've been looking for Splinter. Searching everywhere.'

'He's gone, Chess.' Pacer looked out from under his hood. The sky was like gun metal and he could smell rain. He spat again, irritably this time. 'We've been through this.'

'Splinter was looking for me . . .'

'I know, I know. And Box has joined the enemy. You saw it all through the computer brain before it died.' He swore badly enough to make a cluster of students cross to the other side of the road. 'It's all you ever go on about, Chess.'

'It's not all I ever go on about,' snapped Chess, and any bystander would have been surprised to see the street rat in the black combats step back from the girl with the big brown eyes and wild, curly hair.

He held up his palms. 'OK, Chess. No need to flip.' Pacer knew what Chess was capable of. The big street rats entertained the little street rats with stories of the things she had done to the enemy.

'There's a lot in my head, that's all.' Chess turned round and started walking again. They were nearly at the entrance to the college.

It always felt worst when she thought about her brothers: or at least, the people she'd spent most of her life believing were her brothers. But when she had used the parallax bangle to meet her mother in Knott Street, her mother had told her that she only had *one* brother and that she wasn't to trust him. And then she had looked through the cerebral torus and seen Box with the Symmetry's Dog Troopers and Splinter in Lemuel Sprazkin's laboratory, looking for something. Looking for *her*, Chess was sure of that. So, it was obvious that Box was her brother, the one she shouldn't trust, and discovering this had ripped a chunk from her heart.

'I'll find Splinter if I can. And I'll destroy the Eternal if I can. Without the Eternal, the Twisted Symmetry will never be able to end time. Then it will all be over.'

But she would have to do it all on her own, without any help from the Committee, without any help from Ethel. Ethel had refused to help. She had just wanted to hide Chess away. But Chess was ready to take on the enemy. Months of concentration and practice meant that whatever kind of creature the Committee had made her into, she was learning to control her abilities. She would do things *her* way; she wasn't here to be used by the Committee.

Don't let the Committee betray you. Again.

The words from the Bank's head had lodged inside her own. Whatever else the Twisted Symmetry said, they were right about that.

Chess stopped by the college gates. Pacer loitered beside her and all the students who spotted them there hurried by, swerving towards the opposite side of the gates.

'Jacks.' Pacer spat a bullet of phlegm into the ground and he shook his head before lolling against the gatepost.

Chess leant against the post too, fists in her jacket pockets, one trainer flat against the brick so her knee jutted out. 'Anna's a jack,' she pointed out. Anna's nickname, Fury, had been dropped months ago; Anna might have been a jack but after the attack on the CREX tower, none of the street rats would have dared to cross her.

'Anna's off-grid. She's not like other jacks.' Pacer scowled at a couple of lads until they looked away. It was important to make people like that look away first. And if they didn't, he could always ask them what *they* were looking at. Getting into a fight cost him nothing.

Chess was fourteen now, as well as she could guess, and Pacer was fifteen, the same age as Box and Splinter, roughly. Anna was sixteen, but when she approached with two older girls, neither Pacer nor Chess moved. They just stared, sullenly.

Anna's companions stopped laughing.

'Nice friends,' one of them said under her breath. She was tall like Anna and had yellow hair.

'See you tomorrow, Anna,' said the other girl, shrew-faced and freckled. They walked away quickly, shrew-face darting a glance at Chess as if she had seen her steal something.

Pacer spat.

'It's a wonder you don't die of dehydration,' Anna said to him. Her crystal-blue eyes looked the street rats up and down slowly and she shook her head, the long jet hair with its straight fringe barely moving. Her hands rested on the hips of her school skirt, which Chess thought was too short, and she said, 'Why do you keep turning up and scaring my friends?' But she half-smiled in the way that made Chess glad to be *her* friend.

Pacer smirked. With a hot prickle of envy, Chess could tell that *he* didn't think the skirt was too short. 'It must be the view,' he said.

Anna sniffed and marched away, her hockey bag slung across her back like a rifle. Chess followed, wondering why being friends was such a puzzle for her when everyone else seemed to find it so simple. But she had learnt to live with how everyone liked Anna, particularly Pacer. And Anna *was* her friend; she had helped her even when she didn't have to. She had risked her life to help Chess. And Pacer had risked his. You couldn't get better friends than that.

'Last time we saw you, you said you'd been followed,' she volunteered, walking rapidly to keep up with Anna's long legs. 'By a man with a ginger beard. A big man.'

'Usually it's Chess who thinks she's being followed,' observed Pacer. He had pulled back his hood now, revealing his shaven head. The late afternoon was gloomy but it wasn't raining yet. 'Anyway,' he added, 'we haven't seen you in ages. You've not been down the wharf. Or to Crazy Boris's. Just thought we'd pay you a visit.'

'I haven't seen the man again,' said Anna, testily. 'And I told you, if I need you, I'll find you. I can't have you appearing here and scaring everyone. And my parents would go mad.'

'You're embarrassed by us?' Pacer tried to sound wounded, cleared his throat to spit and then decided not to.

'*I'm* fine about you, but for some reason my parents think you're a bad influence. I can't think why.' Anna softened the jibe by adding, 'And I'm busy. I've got kick boxing on Mondays and Saturdays, kenjutsu on Wednesdays and Fridays and hockey on Thursdays.'

'Don't your parents mind?' asked Chess. She didn't know much about parents, but she thought that night after night of kick boxing and sword fighting was the sort of thing that parents would mind.

'Yeah, they mind a lot, except for the hockey. But they

think it's all part of an aggressive reaction to Richard's death. And d'you know what?'

'What?' asked Chess and Pacer at the same time, stopping as Anna turned to face them.

'They're dead right. It *is* an aggressive reaction to Richard's death. An aggressive reaction to the people who killed my brother. To CREX, or the Twisted Symmetry or whatever they want to call themselves. To Mr Fenley Ravillious.' Her eyes were wet but Chess couldn't tell if these were tears of rage or tears of grief. But she remembered how Anna had promised revenge when she had seen her brother's name crossed out in the notebook that they had found inside Ravillious's desk at the CREX tower.

'How did you find the teachers?' asked Chess, trying to help Anna by distracting her. 'For the fighting. Did you look them up?'

'Yeah, under "Killing, teachers of"?' enquired Pacer.

'I got advice.'

'From?'

'A friend.' Anna was tight-lipped.

'She's gone all secretive.' Pacer smiled but his eyes narrowed.

'You won't tell us who?' Chess wasn't going to play games.

'No. Not yet.' Anna frowned. 'It's complicated.' She wasn't going to linger on the topic. 'But I've been learning all this stuff fast. Really fast, like I'm remembering it: all the kicks and punches, the sequences, the cuts, the katas. I'm good at it. My teachers say I am, anyway. They say I learn frighteningly fast.'

'You're good at lots,' said Chess, a bit glumly and still wondering about the unidentified friend.

'Anyway,' continued Anna, walking again, 'my parents say they're getting me a social worker.' She laughed humourlessly. 'I'm getting them justice and they're getting me a social worker.'

'You still haven't told them about everything that happened?' asked Pacer.

'Are you mad?' Anna screwed up her face. 'Computer brains and inter-galactic organisations who steal children and plan to take over the universe, and people who walk through walls but aren't ghosts?' She looked pointedly at Chess, as if reprimanding her for a bad habit.

'Universes,' muttered Chess. When Anna glared at her she said, meekly, 'There's loads of them, that's all.'

Anna tossed her head. 'If I breathed a word about what was *really* going on, they'd send me to a psychiatrist, not a social worker.'

She turned off the pavement and led them into the woods and onto a narrow track of crushed grass and beaten earth. Plunging into the thicket took them into a viridian gloom laced with the smells of soil and chlorophyll. New green leaves had already unfolded from the trees. The ground was speckled with small flowers like needlepoint, their spring whites and purples leached and tinged brown with the approach of summer.

This was the way that Anna Ledward took Chess and Pacer whenever they visited her. It led through the woods to the bottom of Anna's long garden where there was a summerhouse. The summerhouse was too far from the tall, red-brick Ledward house for her parents to see into it easily and, since they never used it, it was a safe place to meet.

Whenever they took the route through the woods, Chess recalled the first time she had come out this way, out to the Lungs, and it made her skin tingle: tingle with the freezing cold of that winter's night, and tingle with the fear of being abducted by Dr Lache. It was strange how some feelings stayed with you, even when other parts of your life moved on. But it could be good too. Because of the parallax bangle, Chess had been able to meet her mother and that feeling was with her now, forever. She swiped a whippy low branch out of the way and followed Anna. Behind her came Pacer, humming. Chess recognised it, just: a sequence of guitar chords that Crazy Boris had been teaching him.

The path broke clear of the tangled woods a little to the side of the summerhouse. Although the afternoon was leaden, there was a rush of light as the mesh of branches thinned, and ahead of them a long lawn, smooth as the baize on a pool table, rose gently to the high, old-fashioned house with its heavy, cream-painted eaves.

Anna hesitated, crouching. Chess and Pacer crouched behind her. Chess could tell that Anna was studying the rear windows of the house.

'Can't see any movement,' she whispered, even though there was no one nearby to hear her.

Chess couldn't see anything. There were no lights on. The window panes were black.

'Come on. Quick.' Anne strode out of the tree line and up to the front of the summerhouse. It was built of wood, painted green and had a window either side of the door, windows in the side walls and a pavilion-style pitched roof. Chess and Pacer scurried after her, their shoulders low as if that might shield them against eyes that watched from the house.

'Come on then,' urged Pacer at the door when he found it blocked by Chess.

'Shoes *off*,' commanded Anna, from where she sat on the floor inside, pulling off her shoes.

'Well let me get in then,' he complained, shoving Chess out of the way.

Anna yelped as Chess stumbled across her shins. 'You're like an elephant.'

'It's not my fault.' Chess dropped to the floor and began to kick off her trainers. 'And anyway, I'm nothing like an elephant. Elephants are grey. And they have trunks.'

'All right,' conceded Anna. 'You're like a trunkless, *pink* elephant.'

'I can't believe you're bothered about shoes in here. That's such a jack thing to nark about.' Pacer dossed down and tugged off his boots.

'I thought street rats liked bare feet,' retorted Anna. 'You must be turning into a bit of a jack yourself, Pacer.'

Chess liked the summerhouse. It had a rug on the floor and a couple of wooden chairs and a long bookcase crammed with paperbacks whose titles she couldn't read because she had never been taught how. The walls exuded a sweet, woody scent. It was warm. It was dry. Chess knew what it was like to sleep in refuse bins, in drains, under broken walls, shivering in rain; any place with this much shelter was a place to be valued. She brushed her toes over the rug and sitting on the floor as the others were doing, she looked out through the window.

'Just stay low and don't move about,' insisted Anna. 'Mum's in the house. Somewhere.'

'You haven't been to Crazy Boris's in ages,' said Splinter. Crazy Boris: retired rock star and house-proud owner of 18 Mendoza Row, who had offered Chess and her friends a place to stay when they wanted. And they had stayed there, from time to time. But to have a break from his agony at the mess they made, and out of pity for him, most of the time they stayed at the wharf.

It's hard to get away from what you're used to, thought Chess.

'We haven't seen you for weeks,' persisted Pacer.

'I told you, I've been busy.'

'Oh,' said Pacer, as if he didn't mind that there were other things more important to Anna than seeing him.

Anna looked from Pacer to Chess, unblinking. 'It's nearly time. I'm almost ready.'

'For Ravillious?' asked Chess. She saw the kitchen flicker into light. Mrs Ledward passed behind the windowpane.

'Anna, you must be mad.' Pacer shook his head. 'You can't just walk into the CREX tower, you don't know what you'll find. You told us that they'd reset all the access codes after we did the brain. You said you can't even hack into their CCTV any more. And anyway, Ravillious ain't just going to say "sorry".' He looked at Anna earnestly. 'It's proper lively. You'll get slabbed.'

'I've planned this carefully, Pacer,' said Anna as if Pacer

really was stupid enough to think she was going to tackle Ravillious unprepared. 'I've found things out about when Ravillious is there.' She raised her eyebrows, knowingly. 'Thursday nights, he works late in his office, up on the tenth floor.'

'How d'you find that out?' asked Chess. Then, sensing secretiveness, she asked, 'Did your *friend* tell you that too?'

'Yes,' said Anna, 'but there's no point asking me who it is because I can't tell you. Not yet.'

Chess stared back out of the window. Friendship was more complicated than it looked. Except with Gemma. With Gemma, friendship was as easy as breathing. But Gemma was back at the wharf.

'Has this friend told you how to get in to the CREX tower?' asked Pacer. 'How to get to Ravillious?'

'No, no.' Anna picked at the rug. 'That bit's more difficult. I'm working on that.'

Chess had been watching Mrs Ledward, who was standing at the kitchen window. Chess closed her eyes, shrank the distance to the kitchen, felt Mrs Ledward listening. Mrs Ledward had heard a noise. But it couldn't be from the summerhouse; they were too far away. She opened her eyes and said, 'You're not thinking of doing this alone, are you?' It was a challenge, not a question.

Anna paused before saying, 'If the enemy get *you*, Chess, we're all in trouble.'

Chess's eyes felt hot and she chewed the edge of her lip. 'We're meant to be in this together, right?' She didn't know what hurt more: the friend that Anna wouldn't tell her about, or the fact that Anna was planning to confront Ravillious without her. 'You helped me destroy the cerebral torus.'

'Helped *us*,' muttered Pacer.

Chess ignored him. 'I help you get revenge.'

Anna's eyes were sapphire. 'I can't risk you, Chess.'

That's why you've been avoiding us, realised Chess. 'We're meant to be friends?' The words felt clumsy but they were the only ones she could find.

Anna placed her hand over Chess's and very gently she said, 'I know. That's another reason not to risk you.'

'You don't go after Ravillious without me,' warned Chess.

Anna returned her gaze in silence.

A desperate scream electrified the air between the kitchen and the summerhouse.

'Mum!'

Anna kicked her feet into her shoes, burst out of the pavilion and hared up the lawn, her hockey bag still slung across her back. Hesitating only long enough to glance at each other and grab their footwear, Pacer and Chess tore after her. All of them must have crashed through the back door and into the kitchen within seconds.

'A big man. A huge man,' gasped Mrs Ledward, propping herself against the cooker for support. She was shorter than Anna, shorter than all of them, and Chess noticed that this time, she didn't smell of gin. Chess knew that people learnt to live with the damage life did to them. But Mrs Ledward was clearly shaken now.

'Right there.' She pointed to the space where the kitchen door opened into the hallway. 'He was almost naked. He was brown.' And then, gesturing towards Pacer. 'But not black, like him.'

'We can't all be this good-looking,' said Pacer, pulling on his boots.

'A burglar.' Mrs Ledward was trembling.

'Mum?' Anna held her mother's hand. 'A big, brown, *naked* burglar?'

'*Almost* naked. I turned around and there he was.' She sniffed and wiped her nose with the sleeve of her cardigan. 'He ran off when I screamed.'

'I'm not surprised,' mumbled Pacer.

Mrs Ledward dropped her voice. 'He could be anywhere in the house.'

'We'll check,' Anna assured her.

'I'll call the police.' Mrs Ledward straightened herself suddenly, set her shoulders and stared at Chess and Pacer as if she had only just seen them. 'And what are they doing here?'

Chess had met Mrs Ledward once before and she had been nice to her. But then Chess had been arrested in this house for the murder of Oriana Lache; except that she hadn't murdered Oriana Lache, it had been a set-up by the Twisted Symmetry. But Mrs Ledward wasn't to know that.

'Anna, I told you to stay away from these people.'

'It's OK, Mrs Ledward,' Chess assured her, jerking her laces tight.

'It's not OK. I'm calling the police.'

'If she calls the crashers, I'm off,' announced Pacer.

'Not until we've checked the house,' insisted Anna. 'Come on,' and she marched out of the kitchen.

'She can't look for the burglar on her own,' explained Chess, hating herself for upsetting Mrs Ledward and backing away in the direction Anna had gone. She could hear Anna running up the stairs.

'We're only trying to help,' stated Pacer, before he followed Chess and Anna. 'Why do jacks always think we're bad?' he snapped at Chess as they thumped up the stairs. She saw his hand go to the pocket where he kept his knife.

Where the stairway turned, there was a tall mirror. Then it led up to the landing. Anna had vanished but they knew where she had gone because through one of the bedroom doorways there came her voice: loud, angry, uncertain.

'Who the hell are you?'

Pacer and Chess sprinted to the doorway. Chess was first through it and she saw Anna standing on the near side of the bed, hockey stick drawn. On the far side stood a man, tall and powerfully built, his dark torso naked and in his hand, a heavy, wooden staff. Chess recognised him at once.

'Balthazar!'

CHAPTER 6

Chess skidded over the bed and only stopped when her body had flung itself against the solid bulk of Balthazar. She felt his deep laugh, her head rocking on his barrel chest, and she felt his free arm squeeze right across her back. He was warm and smelt of tobacco.

'Wow!' gasped Pacer, who had never before seen Chess touch anyone willingly.

'When I saw you in the trees, when I walked away, I didn't think . . . I didn't think . . .' It seemed so long since she had turned her back on Balthazar and marched towards the surf of the Surapoor coast. She had believed it was a final goodbye. It was good to be wrong. Chess felt her own chest shudder and she clamped her mouth tight.

A hand large enough to cup her skull stroked the back of her head. 'All of us are wanderers in a maze,' intoned Balthazar and with a broad smile he added, 'which means that *always* there is the chance we will meet again.'

Balthazar withdrew his arm the moment Chess took a step back. She studied him intently, frowning at the tiny wrinkles that scored the corners of his eyes, and the creases in his cheeks where his olive skin had been smooth before; the looseness of the muscles that only months before had been slabbed thick across his chest and shoulders and down his flanks; the strands of silver that wound through the long, black ponytail as if it had been plaited with fine wire, and the same silver which flecked his fulsome black moustache.

'You're older,' she stated.

Balthazar Broom shrugged his thick shoulders. 'Once I stepped outside my fate by helping you, time began to catch up with me. I have five hundred years of ageing to do.' But his smile was as bright and broad as it had ever been.

'Aren't you going to introduce us?' Anna stood with arms folded. She surveyed the huge man's scuffed leggings and bare skin and then raised an eyebrow at Chess. 'You may fling yourself into the arms of naked strangers but I prefer to take things a bit more slowly.'

'You're telling me,' muttered Pacer.

'Balthazar, Anna,' said Chess, pointing at Anna. 'And Pacer.' She pointed at Pacer.

'Balthazar Broom, I presume?' Anna marched round the bed to shake hands with the Herculean interloper.

'We met when I was on Surapoor,' began Chess.

'I know, I know,' said Anna. She took Balthazar's large hand in her own, her long fingers wrapping it more firmly than he had expected. 'Balthazar Broom: exiled for five hundred years for your crimes, until you found Chess and her brothers and helped them. Chess has told me all about you.'

'You are a new friend to her?' enquired Balthazar.

'I like to think so.' Anna released her grip but Balthazar

did not release his. His large, bulging eyes peered into hers.

'You are very strong,' he diagnosed. 'And fast. Unnaturally so. This is good.' He released Anna's hand. 'I think your meeting each other was not by accident.'

'We bumped into each other in your maze,' sniffed Anna.

Balthazar's booming laugh shocked her and he held his staff in the crook of his arm as he slapped his meaty hands together. 'Very good, Anna, very good.'

'Is he safe?' asked Pacer, who had not yet put his knife away.

'You're not the first person to ask that,' Chess assured him.

Balthazar looked at Pacer, inclined his head politely and said, 'I see that Chess has been blessed with protection.' He motioned to the open blade. 'But really, my friend, there is no need for that.'

'There's always a need for this,' muttered Pacer, 'if you're one of us.' But he closed the knife.

'Thank you,' rumbled Balthazar and then, as if the knife triggered another idea, he asked Chess, 'Where are your brothers? Where are Box and Splinter?'

'Have you got another five hundred years?' groaned Anna. 'Don't start her off.'

But Chess didn't want to talk about Box and Splinter, not at the moment. It was too complicated. And she hadn't forgotten that Mrs Ledward had threatened to call the crashers. 'We've got to go. Get you out of here,' she insisted.

'How did you get *in* here?' Anna wasn't for moving yet. 'How did you appear out of nowhere, in my mother's kitchen?'

Balthazar's moustache shimmied with a knowing smile

and from the pocket of his leggings he produced a golf ball-sized nest of sticks.

'The tesseract!' exclaimed Chess.

'The very one I found in my house after Box and Splinter had been taken prisoner by the Dog Troopers,' announced Balthazar. He had no idea that the tesseract had actually come from Splinter, that Splinter had stolen it from Ethel at the same time that he had stolen the portable vortex. Balthazar believed that the tesseract had been dropped accidentally by one of the troopers.

'I have some experience at navigating the vortex,' explained Balthazar, with a poor attempt at modesty. 'This device enabled me to find my way from Surapoor to your world, although the ways are many and the perils ...' he shook his head solemnly, ponytail swinging. 'Once I found my way here, to your city, I relied upon my knowledge of your pedigree to track you down.'

'Meaning?' asked Anna, like a judge.

'Where we criminals are concerned, the relevant authorities keep meticulous records.' Balthazar held up a finger as if it was going to speak for him. 'Employing great stealth, I manoeuvred my way into a police station and availing myself of the technology, discovered that this very house was the last location associated with you, Chess.'

'It's where I was arrested,' muttered Chess.

'I am pleased to see that now you are free.' Balthazar smiled hugely. 'So, here I came.'

'She'll be crashed again if we don't get out,' agitated Pacer.

'You'll be crashed if you wander the streets of our world looking like a streaker,' Anna said to Balthazar. 'I'm getting you something to wear, quickly.' She hurried from the room.

'The ... Symmetry ... did not take you.'

Chess saw how Balthazar hesitated before saying the name, wetted his lips as he did so. 'They tried,' she said.

But she heard the voice inside her own head. 'We are still trying, Chess. For all our sakes.'

She shook her head as if the voice was a stubborn drop of water to be shaken out of her ear.

'My prayers have been answered,' said Balthazar in a low voice. 'I had hoped to find you before the end. Last time I left you alone when I should not have done. I do not intend to leave you again. But I see you are safe.' Balthazar rolled his big eyes. 'Thank the gods.'

'Thank my friends,' Chess corrected him, and then pointedly, 'and thank Julius.'

'Like I said,' Balthazar replied, gently, not responding directly to that reminder of his crime, his unwitting betrayal of Julius born of his past obsession with the Twisted Symmetry, 'Mevrad is very clever.'

'Ethel,' whispered Chess when Pacer mouthed 'Who?'

Balthazar rested a hand on Chess's shoulder. 'There is so much for you to tell me, and so much for me to tell you.' He looked at her, looking into her. 'You are a different Chess. Bigger. Stronger,' and he nodded, satisfied with what he sensed. 'Strange how time travels in different directions through our bodies whilst our journey stays the same.'

Pacer snorted and shook his head. 'You jabber proper slash-dot.'

'He's a *philosopher*,' explained Chess, protectively.

Anna returned, a white shirt folded over the black

clothes that swathed her arms. She threw the garments onto the bed. 'Dad's old dinner suit. He's not as tall as you but he is tall. He's got a new one now. He called this his combat dinner suit because he had it when he was in the army.'

She lifted up the silk-lined tuxedo jacket and pointed out the torn elbows. 'Mess dinners,' she explained.

There was a flamboyant lace frill down the front of the white dress shirt. With the collar open and the double cuffs unfolded and poking out of the jacket arms it just stretched over Balthazar's torso. The black jacket and trousers were not as tight a fit as Chess had expected; Anna explained that her dad had been a lot more chunky in those days. But the trousers were short on him, and there were no shoes that would fit.

'You look like a street rat on steroids,' was Anna's verdict.

'Thanks,' said Pacer.

'But it's an improvement on all that nudity,' she added, rather primly.

Chess walked out onto the landing. There was no noise from downstairs. 'We've got to go. Now.' Maybe, from far off, she could hear a siren.

'How do we go?' she heard Anna ask: clear, logical, practical. She must have heard the approaching siren. Or was it sirens?

'Crashers,' groaned Pacer.

Chess could imagine the triumphant smile on Balthazar's face as she heard him say, 'We shall leave by the same way that I entered.'

'Nice,' she heard Pacer say. Balthazar must have pulled

open the tesseract, stretching wide its lattice-work, looking through it to find a gap in the substance of the room through which they could enter the vortex.

But despite the intensifying scream of sirens, despite the activity in the room behind her, Chess's attention was caught by a movement in the mirror on the stairway: a movement that should not have been there since nothing on her side of the mirror was moving.

'Chess.'

The voice came from the mirror, although at the same time Anna called her name from the bedroom.

'Chess,' called the mirror.

Clenching her fists, nails digging into her palms, Chess walked slowly to the top of the stairs and then down to the tall mirror. In front of it, she looked at herself looking back at herself. Then, although she was silent, her reflection's lips moved and the voice spoke.

'Some people will only listen to themselves,' it chuckled. 'They refuse to heed the wise counsel of others. You will find no wisdom in your friends, Chess. Most certainly not in Broom. You know how weak he is. How foolish.'

'I know that you used him. Once,' retorted Chess. But she stayed where she was. Whenever the voice spoke, Chess listened. And it was very hard not to listen to her own reflection, even though she knew that the voice came from elsewhere.

'The police will soon be here, Chess. If you stay you will be arrested. If you go with Broom, the way will lead back to us, eventually.' Chess's reflection shook its head wearily. 'All ways lead back to us, Chess, you know that.'

Tyres crunching over gravel; fists banging on the front door.

'Hand yourself in, Chess. We will come for you and then, together, we can end all this *disharmony*.'

Chess was caught by her own eyes which held her fast before the tall mirror.

'We want peace. Eternal peace.'

It was hard to pull away, even though she wanted to.

'Chess!' Pacer had run onto the landing, behind her.

'Don't let the Committee use you any more,' said the voice.

'What the hell?' exclaimed Pacer, as he saw the reflection talking to the silent girl.

Uniformed figures stomped into the hallway below. He heard Mrs Ledward's voice, breathless, agitated.

'Just make it easy for everyone, Chess,' continued the reflection. 'There's no point fighting. The truth is, you're practically one of us already.'

But Chess knew she hadn't lost herself yet. The enemy knew nothing about what she really was. If they thought she was one of them they were wrong, very wrong. She felt fury sear through her.

'You are *nothing*, compared with *me*,' she snarled, startling Pacer with the deep, guttural voice that roared from her throat.

Chess felt her muscles burst and her eyes were blinded white and then there was darkness. The darkness seemed to bolt up from her stomach and she felt her fingertips slip wet on her palms as her nails cut to bone; she felt her mind hurricane into the mirror, into the voice, smashing its pitch and timbre, as if she were smashing its source to dust.

'Chess!' Pacer had her collar, flinging her to the floor as the mirror exploded in a spray of glass splinters.

And in a place where the dimensions unfolded and shifted like thoughts, the Inquisitor, Azgor, felt the fabric of her soul crack and burn, and begin to slip apart.

'She is too strong. Far too stong.' A voice, a thought communicated through fathomless space, from the Inquisitor Malbane. The Inquisitors' minds were in contact. There were no bodies that could be seen, just energy, shaping, flaring, re-shaping like vast nebulae. Space groaned as Azgor hauled back the bounds of her existence.

'Time is now so short.' Malbane, contemplating, mind unfolding between the stars. 'All we need is a little more, to secure eternity.'

'We cannot get her.' Azgor, reconstituting after the massive blast of energy delivered by the girl.

'We have to get her and we *will* get her.' Malbane's thoughts, running like equations, backwards and forwards in time, simultaneously. 'There is a way, an alternative that I have considered.'

'She is too strong,' lamented the coalescing darkness that was Azgor.

Malbane proceeded with relentless logic. 'Unless a system is perfect, there will always be a weakness. And nothing that is *human* can be perfect. *I* know.'

From Azgor, 'But the girl is not entirely human.'

The equations that were Malbane's thoughts had solved this problem long ago. Backwards and forwards, they had been working to this point.

'I have put in place a mechanism with the assistance of our master, designed to meet this problem.'

'But the girl . . .'

Malbane's calculations surged through Azgor, laying bare his scheme, overwhelming Azgor's objections.

'You see?' explained the Inquisitor Malbane. 'This way we do not have to concern ourselves with the girl at all. Not until she is ours. It doesn't matter how strong she is. The weakness lies in somebody else.'

Pacer's jacket crunched over the sharp debris as he rolled off Chess's body. He yanked her to her feet as the crashers came thudding up the stairs. She looked at him as if the police were not seconds away; as if time didn't matter at all.

'Sometimes,' she whispered, 'I don't know who's inside me.' Then she blinked at Pacer, stupidly he would have thought, if he hadn't been working so hard to steady his jarred nerves.

Without thinking, without knowing what she meant, Chess said, 'Maybe it's my father, maybe that's where it comes from.'

Pacer smashed his fear by grabbing her sleeve and pulling violently. 'You haven't got a father, Chess.' He dragged her into the bedroom where Anna's head and left arm and shoulder protruded out of mid-air as if she was leaning out from behind a curtain, except that what would have been the curtain was the empty space of the room.

'Come *on*,' hissed Anna, beckoning with the visible arm. 'You have to twist your body to get through the gap. It's like a diagonal cut in the air.'

Pacer kept hold of Chess's sleeve. She was silent now: slight, timid, pretty in a wild, chaotic way. Her eyes were wide, as if she was staring at something which terrified her. Suddenly, Pacer wanted to hold her tight, stop her snatching at breath, let her know that whatever happened, whatever she was, he didn't care. He was there for her.

But the crashers were here.

He spun Chess towards him and she came, limply. The two of them followed Anna's arm into the gap in the room that Balthazar had opened with the tesseract. Behind them, the crashers skidded to a halt, agog at the sight of Chess's legs vanishing in mid-air.

After more than an hour of searching, they began to wonder whether they had really seen the street rats vanish at all; they were unaware of anything that could let a girl vanish in mid-air. So, they had to work very hard to convince themselves that they had been wrong about what they *thought* they had seen. But they managed it. There was an open window; that must have been the explanation.

But for some things there was no explanation. So they asked no questions about the lethal drop to the gravel below.

'He has changed.' Skarl stood in a rank of dog-men in the dusty gloom of the Fleshing Yard, waiting for his turn at the machines. He pulled at a coarse tuft of hair that grew under his wolfish chin and then pointed to Box with a long, grey-furred finger. 'Sometimes, I forget he is a skin.' He scratched his chin again, claws rasping on whiskers. 'I forget he isn't one of us.'

Next to him stood a snout called Raxa, heavier, hairier, altogether more dog-like. '*He* forgets he isn't one of us.' Despite the loud whirring of the machines and the grunting of the Fleshings who were working in them, he dropped his voice, mindful of the sharp ears, the hard eyes and the fast limbs of Six, the Yard Master. 'He's even talking like us. Calls his food "slavver" now.'

Six stalked jerkily in front of the waiting Fleshings, his corpse-thin dog face and long, segmented spine swaying out of sync with his scrawny, bow legs. He was a body-length taller than any of the prisoners and he craned over them, his one eye unblinking and the lenses of the scrutator, the optical tube which ran from the other eye socket, through his head and to the rear of his cranium, glowing red.

'Next,' hissed Six, loudly, and the foremost rank of Fleshings stepped up to the machines, whilst those who had been sweating hard at them withdrew.

Skarl squinted up to where the roof of the Fleshing Yard was slashed with daylight. 'How long will they keep us in this pit?' The roof was level with the desert plain above and the merciless sun broke through in stripes, catching the thickly swirling dust within.

'Six says we have another month,' said Raxa, yellow eyes narrowing as he saw the guards at their machine-gun nests in the gantries below the roof. 'Then we get carved.'

'Those what are left get carved,' grumbled Skarl. 'We're down to a couple of hundred now.'

They had started with nearly three hundred Fleshings; criminals and deserters who had been sent to this subterranean training ground on the prison planet PURG-CT483. Here they were trained so that they would be worthy targets for Dog Trooper cadets, who would finally get to wield their mace-blades upon living bodies. As Six reminded them from time to time, 'The cadets have the inestimable advantage of body armour. Not many of you will survive. Those who do will be sent to the Penal Battalions where you will die in a hopeless battle in some distant part of the universe.' And in the other seven hundred and ninety-nine Fleshing Yards on PURG-CT483, the same thing was happening.

The training had been brutal, to instil discipline in the lawless mob of prisoners and to ensure that they would provide the cadets with a hard-won kill. In the mornings, Six inflicted a muscle-shearing regime of sprints, press-ups and sit-ups, stirring up the sandy floor of the vast arena until the Fleshings were choking and the grime clung to their sweating bodies. Then there was sword drill, where they learnt to wield the mace-blade: long rows of them practising to slash, parry, thrust, the short, thick blades glinting in the white stripes of sunlight. After that they were paired off and fought with one another. At first they had used wooden swords, then blunt iron blades, and now they were using the mace-blades, Six stopping each combat after the first cut had been inflicted.

'*He* did this to me,' grumbled Skarl, rubbing a shallow

wound that scored his left flank. He curled up a long black lip as he nodded towards Box, revealing a row of yellow fangs. Box had just withdrawn from the machines and he bent double to catch his breath.

'There were three of you,' observed Raxa. 'You can't complain. He's the only one who has to fight three at a time.'

'It isn't fair though,' muttered Skarl. 'The boy has two blades.'

'He can use two hands.' Raxa shrugged his heavy shoulders. 'He gets two blades.'

'Can all humans use both hands?' Skarl looked at his own palms, as if they were missing something.

Raxa shrugged again. 'He is the best fighter.' He shook his head. 'I never would have thought it.' His dog-eyes blinked slowly, watching the human. The boy was a strange-looking creature, hairless except for his head which had been shaved to a black stubble to keep him cool. Without the fur that patched the snouts' bodies to a greater or lesser degree, the boy's sweat-beaded body looked vulnerable, as if its pelt had been peeled away. But its smoothness was also taut, the hard muscles visible to all. His fangs were small and the claws on his toes and fingers were blunt, but when he fought, his fists and feet were too fast to see and his controlled savagery was smart. The snouts didn't like to admit it, but fighting against Box was frightening.

'He wants to fight his way out of here,' said Raxa. 'He really thinks he can. He has a sister. Her name is Chess. He wants to fight his way out so that he can help her.'

'Must be stupid then.' Skarl switched his attention to the

machines. He and Raxa and their row of thirty Fleshings would be next. 'I hate this one,' he growled.

They worked on the machines in the afternoons. There were three different machines and they were brought into the arena through a wide, iron gate set in one of the otherwise smooth walls. There was the spinacle, which was a series of wooden bars on poles, like turnstiles. They spun so fast that unless you ducked and jumped quickly enough your skull got smashed or your shins broken. And if you didn't stay close to it, Six would rip your head off. Ten minutes in the spinacle and you thought your heart would burst. There was the swipe's arm, a wooden arm on a smooth bearing at the end of which was a long metal blade. You hit the blade and the arm spun round to come at you again, sometimes rotating up and over, sometimes arcing round, never predictable, always whistling through the dry air, slicing the flesh of anyone too slow to parry, or dodge. But worst of all was the blade wall, where, for as long as Six wanted, rows of the Fleshings stood inches before the high wooden fence, and worked to avoid the steel blades that thrust out, unpredictably but lethally.

'We'll all be dead before the carve-up starts,' growled Skarl.

'Next rank,' hissed Six, voice dry as a graveyard, circling behind the waiting Fleshings.

'What are those two doing? They're always muttering to each other.' Skarl pointed to where the Fleshings who had finished at the blade wall were sitting in the dust. To one side stood Box, and close to him stood the tall, lean snout,

Razool, whose dark skin was branded pink on his chest and left arm with the mark of a mutineer.

Box and Razool were talking quietly, too quietly to hear above the grunts at the sword wall, and the thump of blades flashing out and back in. Razool's pelt was black and short, but the ebony hair on his head was long like a mane. Raxa couldn't see Razool's eyes but he could see how earnestly Box spoke with him, looking across to the barred gateway through which the machines were hauled into the Fleshing Yard by the armed guards.

'They're planning something,' said Raxa, but there was no time to wonder what it was. His turn at the sword wall had come.

CHAPTER 7

The rain came in sheets, crashing loudly over the tarmac as if it was being hurled out of the night. The bushes that clustered over the top of the brick wall glinted silver, rainwater gleaming on the thick leaves as it caught the stark glare of the perimeter lights. But at the foot of this section of the wall, where the immense succulents overhung the old bricks, the shadow was deep: so deep that a body could easily vanish within it. It was to this spot that Anna darted after she turned off the main road.

The relentless rattle of rain on vegetation was broken by a long, animal roar from the other side of the wall. The roar came again and then silence reclaimed the darkness. Shoulder against the bricks, shielded by the drooping canopy of leaves and branches, Anna wiped the water from her face and pushed back her soaking hair. Her nose was running and when she sniffed she caught the deep, sweet animal musk and the grassy smell of dung. But she didn't move: not yet.

In her mind she saw the outline of a huge man with short hair and a thick, ginger beard. But when she squinted through the dripping screen of greenery the street appeared empty; she could see no one. Still, she waited for a long minute. Then, satisfied that nobody was following her, Anna tugged the stick-bag to check it was secure on her back before digging the toe of her training shoe into a cavity in the wall. She kicked up, reached for the top and was swallowed by the dense foliage.

Smooth as a puma, she rolled onto her front and dropped down the other side of the wall, just as she had done many times before. Here, the sounds and smells of the city zoo rushed in on her, blotting out the urban cacophony that rumbled less than a hundred metres away.

Squatting beneath an ancient, gnarled rhododendron bush, Anna peered out until she was satisfied that there were no wardens patrolling. Then she bolted across the open park, heading for the high concrete dome that was the monkey house. Again, she heard one of the big cats roaring and this time a bird screamed in reply. Her shoes splashed through grassy puddles that spattered her jeans until her long legs powered her up to a small side door where, panting, she skidded to a halt.

The first thing was to control her breathing: control what happened *inside* to control what happened *outside*. That was what she had been taught.

Water dribbled down her face from her fringe which was plastered to her forehead, but she ignored it. Once her breathing had steadied and her pulse had returned to normal, she slipped the bag off her shoulder. Cursing the zip which sounded loud as a firecracker in the darkness, Anna pulled out the hockey stick. She wrapped her long, wet fingers about the grip, pushed the small door ajar and slipped into the monkey house.

The domed building glowed red and the heat was stifling and thick with the sweaty stench of the chimpanzees. Their silhouettes were visible in the huge central cage, bowling grumpily over the straw, knuckles to the floor, or reclining in the struts and on the hammocks of the vast metal climbing frame that served as a tree.

Facing forwards, Anna used her foot to nudge the door shut behind her. It closed with barely a brush of wood on wood. Ahead of her, a figure worked with bucket and mop, his back towards her. He wore loose-fitting rubber boots and cloth overalls. As Anna stepped into the infra-red glow of the monkey house, he leant forwards, resting on the long mop-handle.

'Good evening, Anna.'

'Good evening, Kinuq,' said Anna, both hands fastening on the grip of the hockey stick now. She rubbed the side of her face against her shoulder to wipe away moisture, and stood her ground.

Kinuq turned, holding the mop in his hands and he bowed towards her. Anna, who was much taller, bowed back. Even in the ruby gloom, the spark of his thin eyes glinted in his leathery little face with its wide cheeks and small, hawkish nose. He approached Anna, boot tops slapping his thick calves. Two body-lengths away he stopped.

Anna sensed rather than saw a small black ball fly at her out of the gloom. Coolly she moved her head to one side and the ball of monkey dung smacked into the wood of the door.

A grunt of disapproval came from the ape who had launched it, and she slapped the floor angrily.

'Your reflexes are sharp tonight, Anna.'

The next ball of monkey dung hit Anna on her left shoulder with a warm thud.

'But not quite sharp enough.'

Then he came at her, swinging the long mop up and then down towards Anna's head.

Holding her stick with both hands, Anna blocked the mop with a loud clack and immediately the cage of monkeys came alive. They barked and shrieked with delight. They ran along the bars of the climbing frame. They danced up and down and they chased one another from the floor to the roof of the cage and back down again in the time it took for Anna to launch a two-handed cut and Kinuq to block it and reply with three head-strikes and a reverse downward thrust at her solar plexus.

Anna swung a low blow that Kinuq jumped before he sprang towards the monkey cage from his left foot. Using his right to gain height, he leapt off the bars, high, bringing the mop down with both hands as he descended. Anna side-stepped fleetly, striking the mop aside, hockey stick in one hand, before delivering a powerful front kick to Kinuq's chest. His feet left the floor as he was driven backwards and he collided with the bucket as he landed.

The chimpanzees hollered in appreciation and slapped their gymnasts' chests with their hands before a baby caught its mother an unexpected blow with a short branch from the floor. Rolling to her long feet, she chased after the chimp, screaming with rage. The other monkeys sauntered away from the bars.

'That was my turn to be taken by surprise,' admitted Kinuq, rising from the puddle of water.

'I cheated really,' conceded Anna. 'That wasn't blade work.'

'Fusion of styles,' chuckled Kinuq. 'I like it.' His eyes glinted. Anna thought they looked much younger than the rest of his face. She replaced the stick in her bag whilst Kinuq unlocked a store cupboard. From amongst the mops and brushes he took a slim case the length of a pool cue. He placed it on the floor before clicking it open.

Anna left her bag by the door and stood by Kinuq, watching everything he did as his hands closed on the sheathed sword that he lifted from the case.

'Flow, movement, balance,' he breathed, balancing the weapon across one hand. 'Hold the saya.' He indicated the curving, lacquered scabbard. Anna took the scabbard in one hand, lowering it to her side. Kinuq twitched a nod and she took hold of the slim, braided grip. On his next command she drew the long, narrow blade, so fast that it vanished, to appear ahead of her hips, angled forwards, dark in the red light.

'Remember, you block with the side of the blade, or the back. The curving edge is too sharp to risk chipping. Just now you used too much front edge.'

Just now I was using a hockey stick, thought Anna. It doesn't have a front edge. But she stayed silent. Over the months she had learnt to listen to everything Kinuq told her, to concentrate entirely.

He stepped away from Anna and flipped over the bucket before sitting on it, resting his hands on his knees. 'When you strike, you must slice: cut *through* your target. Extend your elbows at the last moment, then *drag* the blade.' Kinuq nodded sagely. 'That will maximise the effect. You remember?'

Anna nodded. They had been working on this technique for four weeks. She controlled her breathing and steadied her gaze on an imaginary opponent. Kinuq had taught her that only by using her eyes correctly could she use the sword correctly.

She felt his tawny old face focusing on her intently as she focused on her invisible opponent. When he gave the command, she stepped forwards, delivering a lightning head-strike, stepping back to adjust her stance and then repeating the manoeuvre until her feet, body and arms moved as if they were one with the blade that hissed through the air.

'Good,' said Kinuq, cracking a smile in his hatched, old face, thin eyes narrowing to slits. 'Unity in each movement and each movement part of one. Don't even think of the blade, Anna, it is part of you. There is no Anna and there is no sword. There is only movement and stillness.'

This blurring of body and blade was good. When Anna let go of herself like this and focused only on the patterns of movement, the anger and hurt went away. Her brother and his death washed to the back of her head, never forgotten, but in a place where she was allowed peace. Strange, how working with the sword eased the rage and cooled the fire for revenge. But the fire was always there, hot or cold. Coolly, clinically, every head strike, diagonal upper cut, shoulder blow, thrust and finishing cut were delivered to the same imaginary opponent. For all Kinuq's teaching, it would be difficult to control the blaze when the moment came.

For nearly two hours they worked on Anna's sword strokes, Kinuq occasionally rising from the upturned bucket to adjust Anna's posture, re-align her feet or demonstrate the finer movements. He was patient and, thought Anna, always looked as if he were about to start laughing, although he never did. By the time that the training session had ended, Anna couldn't tell whether she was wet with sweat or from the rainwater that had soaked her earlier.

'Remember to wipe or shake off the blood before you sheathe the sword,' observed Kinuq, wagging a finger at Anna.

She slid the long, curved sword into the scabbard as swiftly as she had drawn it.

'Good,' nodded Kinuq. 'If you can draw and strike as one, that is perfection.'

'Saves time too,' said Anna, handing back the sheathed weapon.

'You must be an economist,' observed Kinuq, boot-slapping back to the store cupboard which he locked once the sword had been replaced.

'You're not really a zoo-keeper, are you?' They had never discussed who or what Kinuq was, before now. Anna hadn't felt it was appropriate, but she sensed that they were approaching the end of their time together.

'You must be a detective as well,' smiled Kinuq. He sat back on the bucket and motioned to the concrete floor.

'Thanks, but I'd rather stand,' said Anna. 'I'm not big on

monkey pee.' She looked at the chimpanzees who had long since lost interest in her. 'You can't really be a zoo-keeper.'

'I am a traveller,' admitted Kinuq. 'Always travelling. I would have preferred polar bears. But this monkey job came along at exactly the right time.'

'The right time for what?'

'The right time for *you*, Anna.' The little man's head jerked to one side, bird-like, as he watched the girl consider this.

'Six months ago, I wouldn't have believed you,' she mused, frowning at nothing.

'Time is the greatest teacher.' Kinuq slapped his thighs. 'All I have to do is remind you of what your spirit already knows. In three more weeks I will be able to remind you of no more.'

Anna nodded. She felt ready now but three weeks was not long to wait. Inside her chest the fire stirred. 'Finding you, using the sword; it's like everything moves together.'

'Sometimes it does.' Kinuq stood up. 'Sometimes.'

Anna looked across to the door. She could hear the rain rattling on the monkey house roof, but that was not why she hesitated.

'All I need now is a sword,' she said. She thought of the giant figure with the ginger beard, and all the night that was waiting for her.

Kinuq stood beside her and rested a strong old hand on her shoulder. 'The sword will find its master.' He patted her shoulder gently. 'Or its mistress.'

Chess stared at the small, framed photograph that hung on the attic wall at 18 Mendoza Row. All her attention was focused on the young woman with the solemn eyes and the dark-brown hair cut neatly to her jaw. The man with his arm around the woman was Crazy Boris, at a time when he really had been crazy. Other photographs and posters revealed him in all his metal glory, but they had been taken years ago. Now he was downstairs, a retired rock star, probably drinking herb tea.

Forty years had passed, but not for the woman in the photograph: not for Esme. She had never been given the chance. They had done something terrible to her, so terrible that Chess's mother, Clarity, had had to be made out of the bits that had been left behind.

Chess looked into the dark-brown eyes of the woman who was her grandmother and asked, 'What did they do to you?'

Each time she asked that question, Chess was answered by a cramping terror, a sense of utter hopelessness, and then nothing. The Twisted Symmetry had almost succeeded in erasing Esme from existence entirely.

But by trying to destroy you, the Symmetry got me instead, thought Chess. And as Lemuel Sprazkin had already explained, the Committee had made Chess into all that Esme should have been, and more.

Part human, part god, part universe.

She could hear his tinkling voice as he added, *and part wickedness.*

Chess reached into the photograph: not with her fingers but with her mind. It wasn't difficult. She relaxed the boundaries between what was her and what was the rest of this universe, letting the space and time spill open. She tracked back, back to when the photograph first came into being, but all the time keeping hold of the fear, the fear that would lead her out of the broad flow of time to the exact point when it had burst into being with all its desperate urgency.

Chess could do this; however she had been made, feelings of pain and terror sought her out, charging her to breaking point. The feelings flooded into her soul as if she was the single focus of all the pain, all the terror. But whereas the suffering would have destroyed other souls, inside Chess it became a raging energy: an energy that could be turned back on the cause of the suffering, with devastating effect. This was what had happened when the Inspector had been ready to kill Gemma at the wharf, when Box had been trapped by the strangler vines on Surapoor, when she had seen what had happened to the children in the Twisted Symmetry's scream rooms and when the Inquisitor, Behrens, had tried to possess her. The difference now was that Chess was learning to control this energy.

She had tried to penetrate the photograph before, to find Esme, and each time Esme had slipped away as Chess's concentration broke. But already she knew that this time was different. This time she was seeing shapes. She felt her heart start to thud. She felt her feet running over concrete, her breathing short: so short there was no air at all. But still her legs were pounding, pounding over the pavement.

Now there was nowhere to run. The alley ended in a wall too high to climb and tall buildings on either side of her, and into the alley swarmed men, or what looked at first like men. Their grey shapes were indistinct and their features kept churning. That was how it seemed, as if they didn't have proper, stable faces at all, and in their hands they carried hooks. The hooks were long and sharp and so black that they looked as if they had been ripped out of space, leaving only darkness. And there were more of these men crawling down the walls behind her and the walls that surrounded her, actually oozing out of the walls, and they all had shapeless faces and swift, shadowy bodies and all of them carried the hooks which promised a dark tearing.

'Please,' gasped Esme, 'Please, no. Please. Help me.'

'Chess.'

Somebody was shaking her shoulder, very gently.

'Chess. Hey, come back. What's wrong?' The soft, confused voice of Crazy Boris with its weary brogue blotted out the men, the hooks and the blurring of time and space. Forty years receded to a small photograph on an attic wall.

'What did they do to her?' sobbed Chess.

'Hey, come on.' Crazy Boris sat down beside Chess and hesitated before squeezing her arm. 'You don't think I haven't asked myself the same question? One day she was there and the next . . .' His hands dropped to his lap and he shrugged. Then he shook his unkempt, silvered hair and scratched the bristles on his gaunt face.

'On the whole,' he said, casting his bagged eyes over Chess, 'I prefer ignorance. Knowing stuff never helps. Unless it's for exams. But being as I never did any of those, I'm not sure about that either.'

Rain clattered over the windows in the attic roof.

'Anna's here,' said Crazy Boris. 'At last. That's why I came to get you.' He cast a glance at the photograph and then back at Chess. 'Looks like I came at just the right time. I don't know what you were doing with that photograph but it didn't look natural.'

'Are the others still here?'

'Oh yes,' replied Crazy Boris. 'The others are *still* here, cluttering the place like a wreckers' yard.'

'Hardly,' smiled Chess, getting to her feet. She wiped her face and tried to pull some of the tangles out of her hair.

'*You* don't have to do the cleaning.'

'Thanks, Boris, for letting Balthazar stay.' Chess didn't want to seem ungrateful for the way Crazy Boris allowed her friends to occupy his sanctuary.

Crazy Boris nodded, swaying to his clicking knees. 'Still don't know where you found that one. Reminds me of what I was like back when I was on the juice. Thinks he's a thousand years old or something.' Crazy Boris shook his old rocker's locks. 'Off his head but he's worth listening to, just for what he comes out with. Don't tell me that's ordinary tobacco he puts in his pipe.'

Chess laughed. 'He's a philosopher,' she said. 'He's full of thoughts.'

'He's full of something,' muttered Crazy Boris as they headed downstairs.

In the kitchen, Pacer was sitting on the sofa, an acoustic guitar across his thighs, and Balthazar sat in dinner suit and open-necked shirt, cross-legged on the floor beside the entrance to the plant-filled conservatory. His staff leant in the near corner. Gemma sat in a fan-backed wicker chair with a glass of orange juice in her hand and a snaggle-toothed grin on her face.

'Anna's here,' she said.

'I know,' said Chess. 'I can see her.'

'Hi.' Anna stood in the centre of the kitchen, rainwater dripping.

'What kept you?' Chess knew that the answer would have something to do with the long bundle wrapped in oilskin that Anna was clutching.

'You look like a drowned rat,' laughed Pacer. Anna shook her head so that her long black hair whipped over him, spraying water.

'If I wanted a swimming pool in my kitchen,' stated Crazy Boris, 'I'd have rung the number for the people who build swimming pools.' He snapped a towel out of one of the kitchen drawers and handed it to Anna. 'Dry yourself with this before we all drown.' Then he looked at where the rainwater had collected in a damp circle at her bare feet. Boris had made her leave her trainers by the front door, together with her stick bag. He shook his head and marched from the kitchen.

'You were meant to be here ages ago,' complained Chess.

'I know, I know.' Anna propped the long bundle against the sofa. 'Hands *off*,' she snapped at Pacer, before his street rat's fingers reached for it. She began to towel her hair.

'You are behaving very mysteriously, Anna,' observed Balthazar, deeply.

'Mysterious is the word,' agreed Anna.

From the brightness of Anna's blue eyes and her breathlessness, Chess knew that something extraordinary had happened.

'Would you like some orange juice?' asked Gemma,

skipping to the unit where the carton of orange juice stood in a sticky orange patch. She slopped more juice into her glass, messily.

'No. Thanks.' Anna threw the damp towel at Pacer as Crazy Boris entered with a hairdryer.

'You,' he said to Pacer. 'Plug this in and get to work on her jeans. I'm not living in a swamp.'

'You must be cracked.' Pacer didn't laugh. 'I'm not Anna's slave.'

'Could've fooled me,' muttered Chess.

'And I aren't touching a hairdryer,' continued Pacer. 'Hairdryers are for girls.'

Crazy Boris brandished the implement under Pacer's nose. '*This* hairdryer isn't for girls. This hairdryer is a piece of old rock and roll. This hairdryer is iconic. If I took this hairdryer to auction . . .'

'So what happened?' Chess wanted to know why Anna had arrived late, to know what was in the bundle.

'That man who's been following me,' Anna began.

'Who you *think's* been following you,' scoffed Pacer.

Anna ignored the interruption. 'He was waiting for me, on the corner of Silicon Chase. I literally walked into him.' She shook her head. 'He appeared out of nowhere.'

'The man with the ginger beard?' confirmed Chess.

'Yup. Really big. And he had a wooden staff.' She looked across the kitchen and pointed. 'Like that one. Except that his had metal on the bottom.'

Balthazar reached a branch of an arm to his quarterstaff and ran his fingers across its base. 'As did mine, Anna. A long time ago.' His big eyes bulged intensely as he looked at her. 'Did this man give you a name?'

'Ragg.' Anna pursed her lips as she tried to recollect the man's full name. She shook her head. 'The first name's gone.' She shrugged. 'He surprised me. And I wasn't taking notes.'

Balthazar nodded sagely and stroked an end of his moustache. 'Might it have been Vladivostok?'

'Yes!' Anna's eyes widened in recognition. 'That was it.'

'Vladivostok Ragg,' pondered Balthazar in a bass, throaty purr. 'How our paths cross, forwards and backwards.' He shook his head, then looked around the room at everyone who was in it. 'All our paths, in a timeless maze.'

There was a portentous silence before Crazy Boris said, 'Deep, Balthazar. Very deep. They'd make great lyrics.'

Chess wanted to ask Balthazar who Vladivostok Ragg was, but Pacer spoke first.

'Did he give you that?' He pointed at the oilskin bundle.

Anna picked it up. 'Yes. You better take this, Boris,' she said, pulling off the rain-beaded wrapping and tossing it to Crazy Boris.

'Thanks,' groused Boris. 'More of your junk.'

Pacer whistled, impressed, as Anna held out the long, black scabbard. A braided, rayskin handle followed the smooth curve of the sheath. 'A samurai sword.' Pacer pushed the guitar aside and jumped up from the sofa. 'Let's see it.'

Anna's warning look stopped him dead.

'Unusual,' murmured Balthazar. 'A nodachi.' He observed how respectfully but firmly Anna took the handle in one hand whilst holding the scabbard in the other. 'The katana is the sword most commonly encountered but a great-sword such as this, a nodachi, is rare and requires a great skill to wield. They are, however, most effective killing weapons.'

'Cool,' sighed Pacer.

'Yeah, wonderful,' groaned Crazy Boris. 'I mean an ordinary sword isn't good enough; this has to be one that's *particularly* effective. If it's alright with you, Anna, whilst you're in my house I'd be grateful if all *particularly* effective killing weapons were kept in their sheaths. If I need any carrots dicing, you'll be the first to know.'

With barely a whisper, the long steel blade was unsheathed, flashed through the air and stopped with only a kiss between its long tip and Pacer's neck.

'Didn't even blink,' boasted Pacer.

'Didn't have time,' smiled Anna.

'Didn't nearly have a head,' flapped Crazy Boris. 'Could you put it away, please? I don't so much mind about Pacer, but that sword could chip the woodwork. And it would be hell getting the blood out of my carpet.'

As quickly as the lethal blade had been released, it was back in its scabbard.

'You're very clever, Anna,' decided Gemma, 'and very accurate.'

'If *she* could pour the orange juice and *you* look after her sword, this kitchen would be a much safer place,' observed Crazy Boris, brandishing the hairdryer as if it was a symbol of tranquillity.

'The sword smiths who can forge a blade like that are few,' began Balthazar. He reached for his pipe which he kept in the side pocket of his tuxedo jacket.

'No smoking,' Crazy Boris reminded him.

'Alas.' Balthazar rolled his eyes and continued. 'To combine the inner and outer blades, to fold the steel skin, to hammer the life into this instrument of death takes artistry and science, and many, many months.'

'Why did he give it to you?' asked Chess. She didn't want a lesson in sword-making from Balthazar. She wanted to know what was going on with Anna. She sensed that it involved more than just the gift of a sword by a stranger.

'He pushed it into my hands and he said the time had come.' Anna tried to control her eyes, but Chess knew her well enough to catch the knowing glance that shot between Anna and Balthazar Broom

'What else did he say to you?' asked Balthazar.

Chess's mind unravelled what Anna hadn't said. 'The time has come? The time for you to find Ravillious?'

'The time for my revenge,' seared Anna, knuckles whitening around the scabbard, warding Chess away from any argument.

Chess was about to ask Anna how she would get into the CREX tower and then she guessed that too. 'He's going to help you,' she gasped, pointing at Balthazar. 'Balthazar, why didn't you tell me?' Chess's voice cracked. 'Why won't any of you tell me what's going on?'

'I've told you already, Chess,' replied Anna, calmly. 'We can't risk you.'

Chess swallowed, breathed deeply. 'We're in this together, right? You helped me; I help you. Friends.'

'It's not about being friends,' Anna tried to reassure her, 'it's about keeping you from the Twisted Symmetry.'

But Anna didn't seem to understand how badly Chess

wanted her to *show* that they were friends. And showing that they were friends meant being there, with each other, when it got lively.

'You don't mind Balthazar helping,' complained Chess, hating how childish it sounded, but not able to stop herself from saying it.

'I am only helping Anna to get into the building,' and Balthazar held out his palms as if they were a peace-offering. In one there rocked a bundle of sticks no larger than a golf ball. 'By the tesseract. She will allow me to go no further.' He shrugged as if his huge frame was helpless against Anna. 'I have explained that more than any of you, I am expendable.' He inspected the backs of his hands which were webbed with wrinkles and he smiled wanly. 'Time now devours me as swiftly as death.'

'When are you going?' Chess demanded.

Anna returned the accusing glare. 'When the time is right,' she snapped.

'Whoa,' intervened Pacer, as if he had only just switched on to the tension. But his eyes were on Chess, her pale face, the rise and fall of her shallow, snatched breaths, the nails that dug into her palms. He hadn't forgotten how frightened she had been after the mirror had smashed, and how that had made him want to hold her, to stop her from shaking. All these years he'd known her and in that moment, when the mirror had blasted apart, it was like something inside *him* had blasted apart. Or blasted into place.

Chess bit her lip. Pacer still wanted to hold her hand, to hold *her*.

'She's only trying to help, Anna. So just go easy on her,

OK?' But Pacer's words fell hollowly into the dead space between the two girls.

'Please, Anna, don't do this without me.' Chess hated herself for begging. 'I can help you. Don't you understand? I *want* to help you.'

Anna marched to the doorway, sword in hand, hating herself for turning away from the girl who was her friend, the girl who had already spent too much of her life alone. But Anna knew that nothing would serve the Twisted Symmetry better than Chess accompanying Anna into the enemy's jaws. She had to be hard, even if that hurt both of them. So at the door, Anna turned and glared at Chess with eyes that were almost as cold as Splinter's.

'I'm going, Chess, and whatever you say, I'm going alone.'

CHAPTER 8

The top of the knife dimpled Splinter's forefinger. With only a minor hesitation, he pushed harder before removing the blade and pressing his thumb under the tiny cut. Out oozed a blob of blood, dark as berry juice. He folded the knife with one hand and dropped it back in his coat pocket before squatting on the pantry floor with his finger an inch above the apex of the Hermetic Codex.

Dr Lache wouldn't wait any longer for him to steal the nexal from Fenley Ravillious. She had become jumpy, nervous even, ever since the disappearance of Boulevant. Boulevant hadn't been seen after the night that Splinter had been attacked in his bed. Splinter was sure that it couldn't have been Boulevant who had attacked him but there was an obvious coincidence between the attack and Boulevant's disappearance. However, neither he nor Dr Lache could fathom the connection. But Dr Lache had become as tense as a trip wire and Splinter knew that it was time to act, before she snapped in his direction.

That was why, within the hour, he would be leaving the house by the lake and making his way south of the city, into the Wreckage. There he would find Ravillious, who would be expecting him. Splinter had found a way to track down the most powerful of the Crystal Priests, but squatting on the pantry floor with the Codex before him was no time to contemplate his cleverness.

Oriana Lache never came to the pantry, not at this time of the morning anyway. Under a large jar of pickled calves' tongues, Splinter allowed the swollen drop of blood to fall directly onto the tip of the Codex where it broke into a miniature rill, barely staining one edge of the pyramid.

Although Splinter counted any amount of his own blood precious, one drop did not look enough. He pressed hard against his finger to extract a further specimen. But before the next pump of his heart, the pantry had vanished and he was squatting on a white floor in a white room, with the bloodied Codex still at his feet. He snatched the Codex and stood up, blinking in the bright light.

The glare eased and Splinter realised he had been standing in the beam of a spotlight. As the beam softened, he saw that this wasn't a white room; it wasn't any kind of room, nor was he standing on a floor. He appeared to be standing on nothing. Radiating away from him in every direction like the spokes of a wheel there were wooden pillars; they soared upwards from his head, fanned out about his body, plummeted downwards from his feet. But the pillars radiated out at every angle too, so it was as if he were standing at the central point of a sphere of spokes, all of them pointing at him.

Squinting, Splinter realised that the pillars were actually immensely long lecterns. It looked extraordinary, particularly on the lecterns that were upside down to him, but perched at the far end of each lectern was a set of head and shoulders, hunched as if studying intently.

There were dozens of these lecterns and along the side of each ran a copper-coloured tube which ended in a flared ring, like the mouth of a trumpet, but much wider. The trumpet mouths surrounded Splinter.

The world beyond the lecterns, the shell of the sphere, appeared to be an eternity of shelves lined with books and scrolls, miniscule in detail and infinite in every direction.

Splinter couldn't see where the light came from, but it felt as if he was standing on a stage. But he wasn't the only thing on this stage. Beside him there was a ball of clear glass, half his height in diameter. Within the ball there were brass spheres of different sizes, all connected to a central gear system by means of thin brass arms, with one sphere on each arm. He counted the spheres; there were twelve in all. Nine of them were clustered in one quadrant. Before he could see whether they were moving, the mouth of one of the many copper-coloured trumpets above his head flickered silver and a voice spoke.

'Under Time-Space Regulation one-zero-four-eight, the unauthorised use of an Hermetic Codex is prohibited.'

Splinter looked up and saw an eye in the centre of the wide, metallic rim of the trumpet. The eye was the size of an umbrella, so the capillaries which scored the white sclera were vivid as coils of red wire, and the variegated browns of the iris diaphragm distinct as tiger stripes. The eye blinked, the sheet of lid flicking closed and open on such a scale that Splinter flinched.

'Who are you?' asked Splinter, aiming his question at the huge eye which peered at him from the galaxy of trumpets.

'My name is Diogenes,' replied the voice, with the condescending tone of officialdom. It reminded Splinter of an unhelpful clerk at the law courts. 'To your right is Phoenix. Beneath you is Old Rumination.'

Trumpet mouths flickered to his right and beneath his feet, and then an eye appeared in each of them: a blue and grey iris in the one to his right and an algae-green one below him. The other trumpet mouths remained dark.

'What are you?' demanded Splinter, stooping slightly before the scrutiny of such enormous eyes.

'We are the Sages assigned to your case,' replied Diogenes.

'My case?' ridiculed Splinter, who didn't much like being called a case. He leant askew as he peered down the side of the tube containing Old Rumination's hugely magnified eye and saw that at the far end, upside down to him, the distant figure was leaning over the edge of his desk with his face hard against the starting point of the tube.

Looking to the right and then up, Splinter saw that Phoenix and Diogenes were also scrutinising him, down the tubes that ran alongside their towering lecterns.

This isn't a stage, thought Splinter, it's a microscope slide.

Diogenes cleared his throat. 'You are an important case, Splinter Tuesday.'

Old Rumination cleared his throat too, with a protracted cough and much harrumphing and said in a slow, bass rumble, 'Which is why you have been assigned three such eminent Sages.'

Splinter stuck his hands in the pockets of his brown

leather trench coat and thrust out his sharp chin. The Sages might have seen through his disguise, even though he had been careful to daub the roots of his hair with black ink as it grew, but at least they understood how important he was. This showed how things were changing, how the King of Rats was advancing in the world. Or worlds.

Splinter pulled a hand out of a pocket and rested it on the top of the glass ball, assuming what he felt to be a kingly pose. The ball didn't move.

'What is this?' he enquired, contemplating that upon which his hand rested, regally.

'That is a pan-dimensional armillary clock,' responded Diogenes, a little testily for Splinter's liking.

The grey-blue eye blinked. 'It measures the time-distance to the fifth node.' Phoenix sounded a lot more friendly then Diogenes. 'When all twelve spheres are in perfect alignment, the time spiral will have reached the fifth node.'

Splinter frowned. This was the type of gibberish that the daft old crone, Ethel, liked to spout. She was always going on about how the time spiral was made of loops with nodes on them and that it was most unstable at the fifth node, which was what the Twisted Symmetry were waiting for. But that stuff was all to do with Chess, supposedly, and how special she was meant to be, and why the Symmetry thought they needed her when the fifth node came. Splinter wasn't here to talk about Chess; he was here to talk about *his* case.

Nevertheless, he couldn't help himself considering the disposition of the brass spheres and observing, 'Doesn't look as if it has a lot longer to go.'

'In terms of cosmic time,' said Diogenes, 'barely a blink.'

All three eyes blinked.

'I want to use the Codex. Why can't I use the Codex?' demanded Splinter, who wanted to bring the meeting back to its proper business.

'It is old technology. It is unsafe,' stated Diogenes.

'Contravenes the second law of thermodynamics, and so on.' Old Rumination harrumphed. 'Offends entropy, you know.'

'No,' stated Splinter, coolly. 'I don't know.'

'Splinter, artefacts such as the Hermetic Codex were constructed without a proper understanding of energy.' Phoenix sounded much younger than his two colleagues, and a lot more patient. 'Such artefacts are based upon geometry, numerology, divination; guesswork. They work, but only approximately.'

'So?' Even an approximate opportunity of avoiding death was better than no opportunity at all.

'The old science is inaccurate,' said Phoenix.

'It's messy. Very messy,' rumbled Old Rumination, disdainfully.

Phoenix continued. 'Whereas a properly constructed device, such as a parallax bangle, takes account of quantum factors, ancient artefacts such as the Codex do not. Which means that their use often generates undesirable side-effects.'

'Which is why they are banned, unless we give permission.' Diogenes blinked. 'Someone has to control these ludicrous machines. Who knows what damage the idiots who use them would do to themselves, or the fabric of the cosmos?'

'Particularly the fabric of the cosmos,' snorted Old Rumination.

'I want your permission to use it,' said Splinter, plainly. 'And I'm not an idiot.'

'Rather a contradiction, that,' sniffed Old Rumination.

Splinter glared down at the green eye. 'It's a matter of life and death,' he stated.

'It always is,' remarked Diogenes.

'This *is* an unusual case, given his proximity to Chess.' Phoenix was addressing Diogenes. Splinter remained silent, despite his immense irritation at the mention of his little sister's name. What happened appeared to depend upon Diogenes, and he didn't want to risk saying anything which might turn Diogenes against him.

'I wonder whether you would look into the cross-probabilities, Phoenix?' requested Diogenes.

'Certainly,' said Phoenix and the grey-blue eye vanished, leaving a dull and empty lens.

Although it was like looking at someone on the top of a high building, Splinter could discern the head and shoulders behind the soaring lectern lean forwards. It appeared as if Phoenix was working at a keyboard. As he did so, the area immediately surrounding the desk illuminated with figures, like equations glowing on perspex. Splinter guessed it was a three-dimensional screen, although he was too distant to perceive any detail.

'Phoenix is one of our newest recruits but he's brilliant,' said Diogenes. 'Prematurely ancient by virtue of his genes; he suffers from Nestor's syndrome.'

'That sounds very unfortunate,' commiserated Splinter, as if he was talking about a cracked nail.

'Not really,' responded Diogenes, equally off-hand. 'That

was how they made him. The sequence for Nestor's syndrome was implanted in his genetic code to accelerate the profound cognitive potential that he already possessed, making him far wiser than his years.'

'*Who* made him?' Splinter was interested now. He watched as a fine, tentacular cable uncoiled from the lectern and dived across the vast space towards the outer shell of endless shelves, burrowing into their contents and depositing a bundle of books on Phoenix's desk top moments later.

Now that his eyes had caught these movements, Splinter saw how similar cables were at work all around the lecterns, uncurling and snaking into the shelves above him, below him and all around him.

Phoenix appeared to consult one of the pile of volumes before tapping further data into the keyboard and then studying the luminous display projected into the space around the top of the lectern.

'Who made him?' repeated Splinter.

'That information is classified.'

'Meaning?'

'Meaning you can't be told it.' Diogenes sounded quite satisfied with this state of affairs.

Splinter didn't argue. He didn't want to upset Diogenes. There was something in addition to the Codex that he wanted to ask him about.

A loud snoring vibrated beneath Splinter's feet. The image in the mouth of Old Rumination's telescope was blurred.

'Either it's narcolepsy or it's old age,' explained Diogenes. 'Old Rumination is often struck by sudden fatigue.'

Plummeting away from Splinter was the lectern, as were

dozens of others. He could see the torso of Old Rumination slumped at his desk, upside down from where Splinter was standing, unaffected by gravity, if gravity existed here.

'He's down to one eye,' enlarged Diogenes. 'Lost the other when he fell asleep whilst writing. Pen went straight through his eyeball. Hasn't stopped him dozing though.'

'Finished,' announced Phoenix.

Old Rumination spluttered awake and his one eye reappeared beneath Splinter's feet, glazed with a film of sleepy tears. It blinked rapidly. 'And?' he enquired with a stentorian croak.

'Taking account of Miesson's effect and allowing for cumulative reductions in the probability echo, we *can* grant authority for use.'

Splinter remained silent. He was interested in answers, not gibberish.

'Are you sure?' Diogenes didn't sound as if this was the answer he was expecting.

'Within all reasonable limits, yes.' Phoenix sounded confident.

'Good,' said Splinter.

'You must understand that there will be consequences,' warned Diogenes.

'To *you*, Splinter,' added Old Rumination. 'By Phoenix's calculations, the time spiral will remain unaffected.' He rattled a cough and the eye seemed to enlarge in the lens. 'You, however, will not.'

'How do I use it?' This was the knowledge Splinter needed. But he couldn't ignore the warning tone of Old Rumination. 'And what, exactly, will happen to me if I do?'

Diogenes gave him instructions in a matter-of-fact fashion. 'Authority having been granted by us for your use of the Codex, the process will continue from where it was interrupted. Since you have already initiated its operation by the application of your blood, you will be looped forwards, to events that have not yet happened. You will see three termination points, three potential termination points that is, and therefore you will recognise any of them should they arise.'

'He means deaths, three possible deaths,' interjected Phoenix. 'The Codex will show you the three situations most likely to lead to your death. These are not the only places where death might be waiting, but they are the three situations where it is most likely to get you.'

'I don't mean to sound ungrateful,' observed Splinter, carefully, 'but I need to know what will get me *away* from death, not what the lead-up will look like.'

'Listen,' continued Diogenes. 'After the Codex has shown you the three termination points, it will return you to where you were.'

'Back to the pantry?' confirmed Splinter.

'If that is where people like you conduct business of cosmic significance,' lamented Old Rumination.

'When you are returned to your ... your pantry,' explained Diogenes, 'you will find the Codex has broken into four triangular pieces. The base plate is waste. It is marked on the inside. Discard it, but retain the remaining three plates. Should you ever be faced with any of the situations the Codex has already shown you, cut yourself with a plate. When you do that, the Codex will calculate how best you can avoid the death that is coming your way . . .'

'In other words,' whispered Phoenix, 'what steps you should take to avoid that death.'

'. . . And it will show you how to do this. Therefore, equipped with this knowledge, you can avoid the termination point that would otherwise finish you off.'

Splinter sniffed, not much impressed by the triumphal tone in which Diogenes referred to his being finished off.

'Each plate can only be used once,' added Diogenes.

'All this messing about with blood, time and numerology,' grumbled Old Rumination, 'very messy. Nothing like proper physics.'

'It's not exactly perfect,' agreed Splinter, trying to sound less critical than he felt.

'We told you, it's old science,' said Old Rumination, disdainfully. 'Nobody asked you to use it.'

'And what happens to me *when* I use it?' demanded Splinter.

'*When* he uses it: did you hear that?' expostulated Old Rumination to his colleagues, rolling his one eye in dismay.

'Because the technology is so rudimentary, it is clumsy.' Diogenes spoke sternly. 'Using the plates will be at some cost, to you.'

'What cost?'

'If you interfere with time, Splinter, time will interfere with you.' Diogenes made no attempt to soften his words. 'Accelerated ageing is the most likely consequence, to some part of your body at least.'

'Using the Codex to avoid death will make me grow old?'

'Or a part of you. And you will only be able to use two of

the plates,' continued the Sage. 'It doesn't matter which, but using the third will interfere with time-space so critically that it will transport you directly to the event you are seeking to avoid.'

'It will kill me?' Splinter had to be clear about this.

'Definitely,' said Diogenes, clearly.

'Another reason for the prohibition,' observed Old Rumination. 'We don't ban these things just for fun, young man.'

Splinter tossed the small pyramid in the air and caught it. 'At least I get to cheat death twice.' Weighing all things up, being a bit older was better than being all dead.

'Possibly. With technology as ancient as this, nothing is certain.' Diogenes sounded doubtful.

'That's everything, Splinter. CASRA will return you to the process now,' said Phoenix, gently.

'To your *pantry*.' Old Rumination even huffed in dismay.

But there was something else that Splinter needed to ask. He spoke quickly. 'Before I go, I've got a question.'

All the eyes were wide open. 'Go on,' said Old Rumination, after a long pause.

'I have consulted the Omnicon and looked for my future and found a blank page.' Splinter looked at each eye in turn before asking, 'What does that mean?'

'The Omnicon should show nothing of the future, nothing at all,' growled Old Rumination, and then, as if there was any doubt about the matter. 'Not even a blank page.'

'Well that's what it showed me,' insisted Splinter. 'Although it wouldn't show anything for anybody else,' he conceded.

'This is perplexing.' Diogenes's eye vanished as the miniscule figure sat back in its chair, high above Splinter, and scratched its head.

'It may be significant,' mused Old Rumination.

'It must be,' replied Diogenes. 'It must be something fundamentally significant: something that goes to the core of the time spiral itself.' The eye reappeared, with interest. 'As I said, Splinter Tuesday, you are an important case. And a deeply worrying one.'

Splinter didn't like the sound of that. He turned on the spot, looking at the big eyes. 'But what does a blank page mean?'

'Probably the obvious,' considered Old Rumination with a hum. 'Loss, nothingness, that sort of thing.'

'But not death?' asked Splinter.

'Different from death,' replied Diogenes. 'But very bleak, I think.'

'Oh yes,' agreed Old Rumination. 'Without a doubt. Very bleak.'

'Well, can't you just take a look?' Splinter swallowed frustration that had a bitter rind of fear. 'You're responsible for time. You must know.'

There was a silence. 'We don't know *this*,' confessed Old Rumination. 'The calculations are inconclusive.'

When Phoenix spoke it was hesitantly. 'There is a chance that the page indicates a choice.'

'A choice?' Immediately, Splinter was suspicious. Whenever Ethel had made him and Chess and Box do something life-threatening, she always claimed that they had a choice.

'There is a chance that an event of intrinsic significance rests with you, Splinter, but that the balance is so fine that the outcome is beyond calculation.' Phoenix spoke carefully.

'That is an alternative analysis,' conceded Diogenes, 'but none of us could predict exactly what this means. If I were a gambling man, which I'm not, I would say that the odds are too close to call.'

'I think it looks bleak, whatever the odds,' tolled Old Rumination and he tutted to himself. 'A very *worrying* case.'

'Just remember, Splinter,' urged Phoenix, 'that sometimes sacrifice can change things.'

'I know that.' Hadn't sacrificing Lemuel Sprazkin to General Vane changed things? Splinter knew all about the advantages of sacrifice.

'We have finished,' announced Diogenes, and the lecterns and the trumpets and the shelves and the pan-dimensional armillary clock vanished instantly, and Splinter was standing on a sand dune with wind rustling through the dark marram grass and low, grey clouds striping the sky.

It took him several seconds to realise that this was the way to the first death. Or the first possible death.

When Splinter moved, the scene jerked like the view through a hand-held camera, and the light was dull and grained like old film. He stepped forwards and immediately, he was at the foot of the dune, as if the film had skipped a run of frames; he was moving outside the normal bounds of time.

A bell was clanging, mournful above the hissing wash of the sea which was as dark as dirty turpentine, and flat under the clouds which bellied just above it. But the sand was white and into view there flickered the hull of a beached rowing boat, standing like a church door, blue paint peeling.

Splinter walked forwards. He saw a table beside the boat, a square card table with a figure sitting at it, its back towards him. The figure wore a cape. The wind droned over the dunes and the bell rang out at sea and Splinter found himself directly behind the hooded figure.

He wanted to see whose face was inside that hood, but when he put out a hand to touch it he found himself in a stone room, as suddenly as if someone had flicked a switch.

Death two . . .

There were no windows or lamps, although it was dimly illuminated. Deep stone arches were full of racks on which were stacked bottles, thick with dust and cobwebs.

A wine cellar, Splinter realised. How would death find him in a wine cellar?

In the ceiling above him the blades of a huge fan were turning slowly.

'I could do with a drink,' laughed a female voice. Splinter looked to see who had said this but the room vanished.

Death three . . .

What he saw next happened very quickly.

There was a man, a tall man dressed in a robe. The skin of his face was loose as melted wax and he had no eyes. He reached into his robe and took out a long knife with a thin blade.

'No,' Splinter wanted to say, but he could say nothing, and the man thrust the knife into his chest.

'No!' screamed Splinter, and he found himself sprawled on the pantry floor. His heart was thumping so hard it ached and with his left hand he felt his chest. No knife, no wound. He gasped and rolled onto his back before opening his right hand to see what it contained. With a tinny rattle, the faces of the Hermetic Codex fell apart from one another.

Four metal triangles, three deaths and one that he would not be able to escape: at least not by use of the Codex. And how many other deaths were there? Having glimpsed the future, or the possible future, it seemed that death could be anywhere and its guise endlessly varied. And having glimpsed the future, Splinter realised that now he was bound to be always vigilant for it, always watching: waiting for the shell of a rowing boat, a cellar, a tall, thin man with no eyes. A narrow man.

Hadn't Chess once said something about a narrow man?

The view of the third death didn't give him much time to react. More than the others, it looked horribly certain. In fact, it had *felt* horribly certain: as if the Codex was showing him something from which there would be no escape. No escape from the narrow man? Splinter shuddered.

But this was the lot of kings, to shoulder burdens that would crush lesser spirits. Splinter had spoken with kings and they had told him this. He would bear the knowledge the Codex had granted him, and use it to his advantage. And the thought of Chess fired him to his feet.

He was the King of Rats, armed now with ruthless brilliance *and* a glimpse of the future. Chess meant nothing to him.

Splinter dropped all four metal triangles into a pocket of his trench coat and left the pantry. He walked out of the house by the lake and onto the road that would take him back towards the city. It was morning, the air was sweet with the fresh scent of the pine trees and deep in the Wreckage, Fenley Ravillious would be waiting for him.

CHAPTER 9

It was funny really, how Splinter had discovered the means to enter Ravillious's house and meet with the Crystal Priest himself. Nights studying the Omnicon had revealed little, but something as simple as a telephone had yielded what he needed at once, although it had been an approach that would have allowed no retreat. But Splinter had been desperate, just like the other players in this game.

'Fenley Ravillious,' Splinter had requested, when he had telephoned the CREX switchboard at the Cones. 'Tell him I have information concerning a nexal belonging to Dr Oriana Lache.' And it had been as simple as that. The chairman of CREX had been on the other end of the telephone within the minute. He was *very* interested to meet the young man who promised to assist him in obtaining the doctor's nexal. And so, Splinter had been invited to his residence, deep within the Wreckage.

Give someone what they most wanted and they'd do anything for you, even if that someone was the most powerful of the Crystal Priests. And Splinter had to put himself close to the most powerful of the Crystal Priests if he were to advance his own ambitions, and stay alive at the same time. Sometimes, being close to the danger was the safest place to be.

Not that Splinter underestimated the peril he was about to put himself in. Fenley Ravillious was the most powerful and the most maleficent of the Crystal Priests. Splinter would be gambling with his life at every step now. And as the Hermetic Codex had revealed, *at least* three deaths lay in wait for him. But finding Ravillious would take Splinter one step closer to what he most wanted: closer to the sort of power that a king should have. Step by step, move by move, Splinter was following his ruthless, risk-riddled but brilliant plan. He just had to stay alive.

Splinter frowned at the concrete structure which lurched up from the ocean of broken cement, twisted girders and gaping pipes that was the Wreckage. It looked like a half-built multi-storey car park. Once this zone had been an industrial heartland, square miles of factories and offices, churning out grease; not that Splinter cared what it had been. He spat out a mouthful of gritty phlegm. Money like that never reached the people who needed it most. Then the dust plague had come, a virus which contaminated the substance of the buildings, poisoned the air and drove out every living soul who did not have to be quarantined or neutralised. The organised destruction of what had been a vast part of the city had razed it to the level of a junkyard: a junkyard that stretched to every horizon with chunks of concrete the size of icebergs and great, mangled ribs of steel, rusting like broken ships.

It reminded Splinter of the wharf after the hunters had

destroyed it, but on a much grander scale. Then again, he considered, these days everything in his life was on a much grander scale.

Splinter had slept rough in the city last night but had been on the move by first light. He had spent all day picking his way across the smashed fields of the Wreckage, heading due south from the west docks which bordered the edge of the Factory Sector. This was the bearing Ravillious had given him and Splinter had navigated it by a compass he had lifted from an outdoor pursuits shop the day before. But all the metal in the Wreckage made the compass needle veer wildly, and crossing the ruins had taken him most of the day. However, now he was approaching a solitary building, or at least the shell of one.

There were other buildings whose shattered remains had survived the obliteration of the old industrial zone. They stood broken and slanting beneath a bruised sky, scattered across the Wreckage like battered lighthouses. By the time that Splinter reached Ravillious's house it was late afternoon and the city was a rough smudge on the northern skyline.

The house, if it was the house, was as tall as an office block. From a distance, Splinter had been able to see through its bare structure but he had thought that close up he would find some solid part, a section that was capable of habitation. Now he saw that save for the area around the entrance, the house was a gigantic scaffold of concrete pillars and partition walls. But there was no other structure standing nearby and he was sure that despite the vagaries of his compass, he had followed the bearing Ravillious had given him.

A series of collapsed walls at the foot of the building

provided Splinter with a flight of giant steps up which he scrambled to the front door. There was, at least, a front door. It was very tall and made of metal which was designed to look like panelled wood. Colonnades on either side gave it a classical look and flanking the colonnades, left and right, were a row of colossal caryatids. They had been cast in cement but moulded with fine detail, from the smooth fall of their gowns to their large, plaintive eyes at the corners of which brimmed perfect stone tears: doubtless shed for the burden of supporting such an enormous weight of concrete on their soft and upturned forearms, thought Splinter.

Splinter could have followed the entrance walls to where they ended and wandered into the apparent emptiness inside the lofty superstructure, but he guessed that that would not allow him access. He had learnt that there was more to the world than his eyes alone could see. He beat on the metal door with his fist and waited.

It swung inwards and standing in front of Splinter was a figure who he guessed was a girl, although she didn't look like any girl, or boy, that he had seen before. Her wide, bony face was even whiter than his own: so pale, so taut that it was like a skull, but webbed by purple veins. Greasy locks of black hair were thinly spread, revealing white patches of scalp save for down the right side of her head where there was a waxy, pink blotch. The girl was a head shorter than Splinter. 'My father is waiting for you,' she said, the eyes with their livid, violet irises fixing him with the dead intensity of a shark.

'Sorry I'm late,' mumbled Splinter, momentarily wrong-footed by the weirdness of Ravillious's daughter.

'Come in.' She hadn't even blinked yet.

She was wearing a cheap, blue tracksuit and a pair of trainers but what Splinter noticed was what she wore on her middle finger: a silver ring engraved with the C of the CREX Corporation. He had studied the Omnicon closely enough to identify a nexal when he saw one. The awful reality that there were two Crystal Priests here dawned on him. He should have realised that Ravillious's daughter might be in the same place as Ravillious. But the Omnicon had provided him with scant information about her.

Suddenly, this had become a lot more lively.

'Come in,' repeated the girl in the same dead voice and Splinter was relieved to see that at last she blinked, shielding him momentarily from those cadaverous eyes.

He stepped into the house and behind him the door closed with a soft thud. He was in a hall, vast as the atrium of the city post office. It was cool and airy with a floor of black marble flecked with grey. White pillars supported the high ceiling. The light was low and easy but Splinter couldn't see where it came from; it seemed to seep from the bare walls themselves. Up one wall there ran a highly polished steel staircase. At the top it turned onto a landing, galleried by marble colonnades. But the girl walked across the black floor of the hall to one of the many passageways that led from it, and a little distance behind her, Splinter followed.

There were no decorations, no ornaments, no paintings, no rugs. The corridors were plain, floored with the same cold marble and swallowing the sound of their footfalls effortlessly. Long, high windows rendered views across the Wreckage, colouring them with a slight ochre tint.

This was a house you could see out of, but not into. Splinter liked that.

He kept count of the steps they took and the corners they turned but found that although he was well-practiced in this habit, the house confounded him. There were times when he looked back the way they had come to discover that what had been a long corridor was actually a doorway, what had been a flight of stairs had become a plain wall. At first he had assumed the mistake was his, but quickly he realised that it was the house. The house didn't stay the same.

'This way,' said the girl, dully, when she saw Splinter staring at a wall that had dissolved into a long gallery, evening sunlight flooding its massive windows. It was the first time she had spoken since they had begun their trek through the house.

As Splinter passed by the next door, a noise caught his ear: a scratching, scrabbling noise, down at the bottom, where the metal door met the floor. He paused, head askew as he wondered what was on the other side. It sounded as if something was trying to get out. Observing that the girl was still walking ahead, Splinter put his hand over the doorknob and pushed gently, but there was no movement. The door must have been locked.

The scraping at the foot of the door became frenzied.

Curious, Splinter pushed his ear against the metal. The scratching stopped and then something crashed into the other side of the door. There was a shrill screech and a frantic clawing.

Splinter leapt away. Quickly, the noise diminished into a sporadic scraping and then it stopped. Splinter hurried after the girl and when he looked back, the door had vanished altogether. He meant to ask her about the scratching at the door, but as he opened his mouth, the walls about them shifted colour from white to a throbbing red.

'What's wrong with this place? Why won't it stay the same?'

The girl didn't turn round but she did stop walking for a moment. 'Something has upset my father,' she said, and Splinter was relieved when the wall returned to white.

Obviously, the house was very much larger than it looked from the outside but that didn't concern him; he had grown accustomed to this sort of spatial weirdness. However, its tendency to transform doors into walls and corridors into windows did unsettle him, and after the scratching noises, the skin on the back of his neck prickled with the sense of being watched. It felt to Splinter that this was a house that could see.

'Up here.' The girl stepped into a narrow stone staircase that ran up so high, Splinter couldn't see where it ended. His stomach rumbled.

'I'm hungry,' he complained, in case the girl hadn't heard his guts. 'I've been walking all day.' But he joined her on the staircase and as he did so, the step on which he stood swept upwards, seemingly passing through the steps beyond, or they were passing backwards through it.

'Whoa!' whooped Splinter, dropping to a crouch as he found himself at the top of the staircase that now plummeted down from them.

'In there.' The girl pointed.

Treading cautiously, as if the marble floor might give way

at any moment, Splinter entered the room. It was as huge as the other rooms in the house but its ceiling was much lower. There were windows all the way round, slanting inwards from bottom to top, and the evening sun was caught in the west windows so brilliantly that Splinter was blinded by it.

'Hello, Thorne,' came a voice from the opposite end of the room. A cool, sonorous voice. 'I am Fenley Ravillious.'

Splinter advanced, shielding his eyes.

'Sorry about the light.' And at once the glass in the windows darkened, polarising and turning the outside world magenta.

Now, Splinter could see the shattered plains of the Wreckage and the smoking smudge of the city to the north, stained gentian by the glass. Dust particles drifted aimlessly in the sunlight that filtered through the windows. The stillness was broken by Ravillious's deep, hard voice. 'Come here, Thorne.'

Fenley Ravillious sat on a high stool at a workbench that ran almost the length of the north windows. He wore jeans and an open-necked shirt of pink, the sleeves loosely rolled halfway up his forearms. His steel-grey hair was smoothed back from his tanned, wrinkle-scored face. In his hands he held a pair of tweezers and a scalpel.

Crossing the room, Splinter saw that on the workbench, immediately beside Ravillious, there was a row of tall clamps supporting an assortment of hanging shapes that he couldn't recognise. Around the clamps were small spotlights and optics, like enormous magnifying glasses, and gathered about this apparatus were little heaps of what looked like metal and wire and blowtorches and at least one set of goggles.

Then Splinter saw the bird and he stopped dead. It sat on a perch above the bench and was watching him through sharp, black eyes. It was larger than an eagle, with plumage as brilliant as a parrot's, but its hooked beak glinted like steel and its talons were like spurs. When it saw Splinter looking back, it spread its huge wings with a metallic rattle and cawed once.

Splinter thought of the door and the scratching sounds.

'His name is Archaeopteryx. I made him.' Still holding the tweezers, Ravillious dipped his fingers into a china bowl and then flung a steak-sized chunk of wet meat into the air. The great bird snapped at it, rending it to shreds in its sharp beak in seconds.

'Archaeopteryx is as big as they come. He is my favourite. But I have made hundreds. I find it a relaxing pastime.'

Up close, Splinter could see that hanging from the clamps were small leaves of metal connected to minute wires, some of which trailed to an item at one end of the array that looked like a fibrous tangle of roots.

'You see this, Thorne?' Ravillious indicated the bristling fibres with his tweezers. 'This is the central nervous system of a bird, a magpie in this case. Here is the brain, the spinal cord,' Ravillious continued to point with the tweezers. 'See the dendrons, ganglions? It is a painstaking but therapeutic activity to insert this into the metal shell.'

'It must be very complicated,' said Splinter, seeing now just how many wires there were.

'Neural sculpting is inhumanly complex,' drawled Ravillious with half a smile. 'I should like to do it with a human though.' He studied Splinter so intensely that

Splinter felt his flesh crawl. 'What would it feel like for your nerves to be soldered to titanium and to live?'

Splinter swallowed. 'Uncomfortable?' he suggested.

'Doubtless. Which would account for the metalbacks' aggression.' Ravillious flung another lump of meat into the air. Archaeopteryx snatched it in his talons and tore. 'What are they for?' asked Splinter.

'Killing,' said Ravillious. 'Killing people.'

'Oh.' Suddenly, Splinter didn't want to ask what Ravillious was feeding it.

'I graft tongues into their maws.' Ravillious put down the tweezers, licked his bloodied fingers and swept back his hair. 'A sense of taste is necessary if they are to do their work, although my engineering doesn't do justice to the natural variety of receptors.'

'Your house is unusual.' Splinter wanted to change the subject from what the metalbacks ate. His own hunger had vanished once he had seen the gory contents of the bowl.

'I. A.,' said Ravillious, as if that might mean something to Splinter.

With a creak of his trench coat, Splinter folded his arms. 'Meaning?' It was time to look a little less astonished by everything about Ravillious and his house, even if that was how he really felt.

'Intelligent Architecture.' Ravillious's face lost any trace of amusement it might have been exhibiting and Splinter realised that the folded arms were a mistake.

The walls of the room darkened.

'This house is built of smart particles: programmable

matter containing neuroreceptors which respond to my brain patterns.'

'Meaning?' But this time, Splinter's voice caught in his throat.

'Meaning,' said Fenley Ravillious, with a purr, 'that it does whatever I think.'

Suddenly there were walls all around Splinter, coffin-close. They had come from nowhere and now he couldn't move. He couldn't even unfold his arms.

'I'm not going to leave you in there, Thorne.' Ravillious chuckled from outside the marble sarcophagus. 'But I like the thought.'

The walls were absorbed back into the floor and as Splinter lowered his arms and stopped himself from wondering whether he shouldn't remove himself from this slash-dot slab-job now, Ravillious was leaning down from his stool and reaching into a container below the bench. The lid had been slipped open and vapour steamed out.

'Liquid nitrogen,' said Ravillious, plunging his bare arm into the freezing contents. He lifted out a small glass tube, and flicked the lid back onto the container with the toe of his boot. 'See? A tongue.' He held up the tube in his hand which was crusted with ice. 'The biological material must be stored cryogenically.'

'Why couldn't I see your house from outside?' Splinter dared to ask.

'You'd like that, wouldn't you, Thorne? Being hidden, like my house. Any thief would like that.' Ravillious prodded the tips of the tweezers into the tube.

Archaeopteryx uncurled and curled his talons and cawed

softly, watching the purple stub of bird tongue with sniper-like intensity.

'This building is a piece of mathematics.' The Crystal Priest bent over the nest of nerve fibres. 'It is a contradiction. Its coordinates have been plotted so that it is simultaneously here and not here, simultaneously "and" and "not", you might say. Which means it is hard to observe, even for an Omnicon.'

'So your house is hidden from *everything*?'

'From everything on the outside, yes,' came the softly spoken reply. The Crystal Priest was concentrating on his work. 'Sometimes a contradiction like this is partial. Sometimes it only works when you approach it from a particular direction. But this one, my house, is nearly perfect.' The tweezers picked, minutely.

Splinter's lips were dry. He licked them. 'Is it warp technology?' he asked, tempted to know more. 'And the neural sculpting, is that warp technology too?'

'You know about warp technology, do you, Thorne?' murmured Ravillious, dangerously, and Splinter cursed himself for revealing too much about what he knew. But Ravillious answered his questions. 'Neural sculpting is an extension of a process employed by the warps, yes. But the mathematics behind my house is something I designed myself.'

There was a metallic clicking and then a sound like sticky banana being mashed. 'One tongue beautifully inserted between metal and nerves.' Ravillious placed his implements on the bench and turned round. 'Shall we get down to business, Thorne?'

'By all means, sir.'

'You said you can help me take Dr Lache's nexal?'

Splinter nodded, relieved to see that Fenley Ravillious was this interested, but also a little baffled that the Crystal Priest did not question him about how he came to occupy such an intimate position with Oriana Lache, or how he would achieve such a feat. Which meant, at least, that Splinter did not have to reveal that he possessed a portable vortex.

'And why do you want to help me?'

'Because you are more powerful than any of the others,' answered Splinter. 'And because I like to be on the winning side.' Which was true. When Ravillious kept staring at him with his lizard eyes, Splinter added, 'I know what's going on, sir.'

'Do you, Thorne?' Ravillious rested his elegant but capable hands on the thighs of his jeans, the nexal with its signature C worn on the middle finger of his right hand. He said, 'It seems to me that you know a good deal more than you are ready to tell.'

Splinter braced himself for whatever might happen next but nothing did happen: nothing bad. Ravillious smiled, a bleak, cold smile, but it was a smile nevertheless. 'Any good thief will know more than he tells. Although,' and here the smile vanished, 'he should take rather more care to hide that fact than you do, Thorne. Strange, I would have expected you to be smarter.'

Splinter's pallid cheeks burned but he forced himself to stay silent.

'Let me tell you how we shall play this, Thorne.' This was

a man well used to giving orders, to being in command, but polished by the assassin-civility of the boardroom. 'You shall take my nexal to Dr Lache: that is, a ring that you will tell her is my nexal ...'

'But she'll know if it isn't ...'

Ravillious held up a hand to staunch the interruption. 'Leave that to me, Thorne. When you give her the nexal you must convince her to come to my house.'

'How shall I do that?'

'That is a problem for you, Thorne. If you fail to get her here, all your machinations will come to nothing. But I am sure it will be easy for you to entice her here, once she knows how weak I must be without my nexal. Once you get her here, Tethys and I shall be waiting, all our power intact, of course.'

'Tethys is a Crystal Priest too?' Splinter feigned surprise, attempting to regain some ground by appearing more ignorant than he really was.

'Don't be stupid, Thorne. Your sharp eyes won't have missed the nexal on her finger. But I tell you this: there is more to Tethys than the ring she wears. She has power of her own and she loves me: loves me with as much heart as she possesses.'

Splinter was taken aback by the passion with which Fenley Ravillious spoke. He looked over his shoulder to where the girl sat, where the top of the stairs met the entrance to the room, her back against the wall and her chin in her knees. Obedient. Waiting.

Ravillious brushed back a steel lock of hair and rubbed his weathered cheek. 'You will accompany Dr Lache. You will *make sure* she comes here. You will not let her turn back. *Whatever* happens, *whatever* comes towards you, you must not let her turn back. Do you understand?'

'Yes, yes. I understand, sir.'

'When it is over, when I have her nexal, you will have earned your place with me.'

'Do I *have* to be with her?' asked Splinter. 'I mean, even if it gets messy?'

Ravillious leant forwards. So did Archaeopteryx, and Splinter couldn't help noticing how similar their eyes were.

'Yes you do, Thorne.' Ravillious's stare almost flayed him. 'You must make sure nothing stops her, nothing lets her turn back.' The Crystal Priest permitted himself a sardonic twist of his lips. 'She trusts you, Thorne. What a terrible mistake.'

To be standing before someone who read him so well made Splinter feel as if his insides had been dragged out.

Ravillious took an object from his jeans pocket and tossed it to Splinter who snatched it as surely as Archaeopteryx snatched meat.

It was a ring, engraved with the CREX emblem, identical to the ones worn by Ravillious and his daughter.

'You can go now. Tethys will show you out.'

Fenley Ravillious stepped off the stool and stood looking north, arms folded. Night was stealing across the distant city whilst an oxblood fire tore the western horizon. 'Remember, Thorne, on no account is she to turn back.'

Splinter couldn't help himself from asking, 'Why? Why would she turn back?'

'Exactly, Splinter,' whispered Ravillious. 'Why would she?' But the Crystal Priest offered no further explanation.

Splinter put the ring in the pocket of his own jeans and he crossed the marble floor to where Tethys was standing, his gait uneven because of his slight limp.

'Follow me,' she said, without even looking at him.

'Of course I'll follow you,' Splinter muttered at her back. 'How else am I going to get out of this stupid house?'

This time the stairs retained their form and Splinter marched down them in an ill temper because now he was hungrier than ever.

'Is there any chance your father could think up a kitchen?' He didn't expect a response. 'Do you people eat? Do you have stomachs? I've got a stomach, can't you hear it?' He plodded down the corridor morosely. 'It makes better conversation than you do,' he muttered.

Tethys turned round then and spread her hand in his direction. The fathomless eyes that hollowed her broad skull widened and a door surfaced out of the wall to Splinter's left. A metal door.

A door with a clawing thing on the other side.

'What?' Splinter managed to shout before his body was thrown into the room. He crashed across the floor and the door slammed shut.

At first he heard only his own breathing but he knew that the darkness had eyes.

'Oh no,' he whispered, remembering how the metalback's titanium beak had shredded the chunks of meat.

The darkness began to shriek and the claws came for him.

CHAPTER 10

Metal wings beat the air, whirring all about him. Splinter curled into a ball. He felt his leather coat tear across his back from shoulder to hip, and an instant later he felt the pain scorch down the line of the rip. His upper arm was in an iron grip which encircled triceps and biceps, another set of talons punctured his left calf and now there were claws in his hair, scrabbling around the side of his head and towards his face.

The momentary thought that he could not be about to die because the Codex had never revealed this was no comfort. The Codex only showed possible deaths, not *all* deaths. And what was happening now was all too real. The darkness was full of wings and claws, the claws were tearing his clothes to get at his flesh and his face was wet with his own blood. He felt something knife into his upper arm and then, all over his body, the metal beaks got to work.

'No!' screamed Splinter, rolling across the floor, unable to shake off the creatures that had fastened themselves to him.

Then there was a rectangle of light and in the light stood a figure. There was a rush of air as the metalbacks lifted off his body as one and returned to their roosts in the darkness. Groaning, he wiped the wetness out of his eyes and then he saw that it was Tethys standing in the doorway.

Splinter swayed to his knees. The pain was like molten lead, on the back of his head and sides of his face, over his shoulders, down his back and arms, across his chest and over his legs. His leather trench coat hung in tatters and the slashes in his clothing were wet with blood from the wounds beneath.

'Why?' he gasped.

'You don't think any thief could steal my father's nexal without a fight, do you, Thorne?'

Splinter staggered towards the doorway.

'Lache must *believe* you stole it. She must see the damage, see the pain.'

Splinter stumbled into the passageway and gasped as he saw the bloody mess he had become. Then the floor gave way, or seemed to give way, and he spun through space to find himself facing the front door of Ravillious's house. The door was open and outside was the night, a bright fuzz of orange to the north where the city lit the sky like streaks of crayon.

'Now get out,' whispered Tethys, shoving Splinter in the small of his back. He couldn't tell whether it was her hands or her mind that had done the shoving but the force was sufficient to send him somersaulting down the slabs of concrete he had used as steps a couple of hours before. His fall was broken, eventually, by a rusty length of pipe. He lay against it, letting the cool metal soothe his burning face and looking up at the clear sky which was prickling with stars.

He started to laugh although he wasn't sure why.

'What are you doing?' he asked himself, looking back the way he had fallen, seeing the towering skeleton of the house. Then the pain began to hammer his nerves and he stopped laughing.

'They shouldn't have done that,' he hissed, beginning to stir his arms and legs. 'Nobody treats the King of Rats like this and lives.' But it took the King of Rats three attempts before he could stagger to his feet and stay on them.

'Thorne! What have they done to you?'

Splinter was barely conscious as Oriana Lache helped him out of the battered taxi.

'Pay him,' mumbled Splinter. 'Pay him what he asks.'

'How much?' asked Dr Lache.

The driver licked his lips. He had only half-believed it when the bundle of blood and rags had shambled up to him from the edge of the Pit that evening and asked for a ride to the Lungs. He'd said it was a slab-job gone wrong, that the regulars, the grown-up crooks, were coming for him but that there was a bucket of grease for the driver who could get him out.

To the drivers, a fare was a fare; nobody would fillet them for earning their living. So after lining the back seat with polythene, he had driven his clanking wheels out here. And now was his chance to cash in on the gamble.

He licked his lips again. 'Two hundred.'

'Fine.' The elegant woman hurried back to her house, smooth, graceful, and the driver cursed himself for not asking for more. When she came back she paid him in crisp notes and he caught the smell of her perfume: clear, clean, sophisticated.

'You want a hand?' he asked, nodding at the body, slumped against the side of the car.

'No, thank you.' The lady smiled politely. Nice teeth. She put an arm round the fare's torso and hoisted him to his feet, helping him to the front door.

The driver rubbed his face and whistled low through his nicotined teeth. That lady was as strong as she was pretty. Then he climbed back into the saloon and coughed away in a blue fug of engine oil.

Eyes closed, Splinter noticed the smells, the scent of resin, the sweet aroma of wood, Dr Lache's perfume. They were reassuring because they were safe.

Safe! The thought nearly set him laughing again. He had passed from the clutches of one Crystal Priest into the arms of another. Safe was the one thing he wasn't. And yet, as he was propped in a chair in the bathroom and his clothing peeled away from him, that was how he felt.

'I'm thirsty,' he croaked.

'Yes, yes you must be.' Dr Lache shook her head. 'How much blood have you lost?'

'Most of it,' groaned Splinter, blinking into the white light.

Dr Lache passed him a glass of water and he gulped it down messily, the trickles burning where they dribbled from his chin onto his lacerated chest. He drank another glass and now his head really began to thump.

Oriana Lache set to work with cotton wool and antiseptic

that scorched like acid, and a needle and thread on the deepest gashes.

Strange, thought Splinter, how she hasn't even asked me about the nexal yet. Dr Lache seemed more concerned about what had been done to him.

'How did this happen?' she asked.

'I found my way in,' explained Splinter, employing his rich talent for lying, 'and discovered that it was a house that moved with a mind of its own.'

'How did you get in?'

Splinter managed a modest smile. 'I am a thief like no other.'

'I don't know what to make of you,' admitted Dr Lache, and then, as if she had only just recalled what this was all about, she asked breathlessly, 'Did you get it?'

Splinter nodded slowly and despite his wounds, he enjoyed the way Oriana Lache gasped with delight and her face, normally so demure, so composed, lost all its restraint for a few moments.

'You are wonderful!' She clapped her hands together and kissed him on his claw-raked forehead. The kiss burnt, but not in the way the antiseptic did.

'Can I see it?' she asked.

'In a moment.'

Splinter was surprised because Dr Lache just nodded and said, 'Of course, of course. First things first. We need to get you straight.'

'Can't you just use your power to fix this mess?'

'I could,' said Dr Lache, 'but I want you to be you.'

Splinter couldn't fathom that response but at her request

he continued with his story. 'The house does whatever Ravillious thinks.' He winced as needle and thread set to work on his right shoulder. 'Because the house saw me, so did Ravillious, and he came for me. He turned the windows on me, at least, that's what it seemed like. All the glass exploded and came at me like knives.' It was important not to blame his injuries on the metalbacks; there would have been no reason for the metalbacks to have stopped until his bones had been picked bare.

'I'd hoped to use my stealth.' Splinter shook his head forlornly. 'Ravillious's house didn't let me do that. But,' and here he allowed a triumphal sneer to enter his voice, 'I knew that Ravillious would be confident he was smarter than me.'

'Oh yes,' agreed Dr Lache, most earnest, 'he would think that.'

'And I knew my blood would be irresistible to him.'

'Yes.' Oriana's face darkened. 'He would have no appreciation of your other qualities, Thorne. He would see you only for your energy.'

'My blood!' cried Splinter, startling Dr Lache. 'That's what I shouted, "My blood! My blood is *everywhere*!", and that's when Ravillious came to me, knelt by me, told me what he would do to me.'

'Yes, yes,' hissed Dr Lache, coldly, 'that's exactly like him.'

'He put his hand on my throat.' Splinter sniffed contemptuously. 'Even a man like Fenley Ravillious is predictable. I tried to prise his hand away, at least, that is what he thought I was doing. But what I actually did was to take this,' and Splinter took the ring from his pocket and held it up.

Oriana Lache gasped and stepped back.

'He was so busy throttling me, he paid insufficient attention to what the cleverest thief in the universes was doing.' Splinter's fist closed about the ring. 'You see, his hands were slippery with my blood. It wasn't difficult to slide the ring off his finger in the struggle. I stabbed him with a piece of glass as he begged for mercy.' Then Splinter added a crucial detail. 'He was still alive when I left him. He may be alive still for all I know.'

'Where did you stab him?' Dr Lache spoke urgently. Splinter had to make sure she bit on his devious little hook.

'In the arm, I think. It was hard to tell because it was dark and my eyes were full of blood and I just managed to get away. And I remember what he said as I left him there: something about, "I will let her know what has happened. She will come to me. *She* will help me".' Splinter shrugged as if baffled by what Ravillious meant, and gasped as the fresh stitches snagged the skin of his shoulder. 'Did he mean you?'

'No.' Dr Lache's eyes were livid. 'He meant that creature he calls his daughter.'

'I'd forgotten about her!' exclaimed Splinter, quite enjoying the lightning effect of his mendacity.

'Tethys, remember?' Dr Lache bit her lip before making her decision. 'We must go to his house as soon as you're able.'

Deep inside, Splinter relaxed; Dr Lache would go to the house, just as Fenley Ravillious had demanded.

Dr Lache spoke quickly now, her mind made up. 'We must ensure Ravillious is finished, dead, before Tethys finds him.

But I need you to take me there. You have the knowledge.'

She set down the needle and thread and ran her arms over the tears in Splinter's skin, down his arms and legs, pressing her palms against his back and then his chest.

'What are you doing?' asked Splinter.

'I need you well, I need you fit, right *now*. We no longer have time to enjoy the luxury of pure time.' She cupped Splinter's chin in her hand and held his eyes in her own. 'The cuts on your face and the wound in your shoulder will be a memento of what you have done for me. The rest must be healed by their power.'

Memento or not, Splinter would rather not have been left with any scars. But he didn't want to do or say anything that might distract Oriana Lache from the course on which she was now set. However, he couldn't resist asking, '*Their* power?'

Oriana Lache touched the nexal around her neck before returning her hand to Splinter's face. 'The Inquisitors,' she whispered. Then her fingers brushed his torn flesh again. Her hazel eyes closed and Splinter felt his wounds itch and crawl. When Dr Lache opened her eyes seconds later, Splinter saw that the metalbacks' blood-work had vanished from his body and arms and legs. All that remained was an expertly stitched incision in his right shoulder and a tramline gash from his forehead to his right cheek.

The doctor's fine hand was lowered, but it remained open. 'Please, Thorne, the nexal.'

'I will give it to you,' responded Splinter, 'once I have consulted the Omnicon. And once I am fully dressed.'

Dr Lache bit her lip but didn't argue. Splinter knew why:

she trusted him, just as Fenley Ravillious had said, although how Ravillious could have been so sure of this, Splinter had no idea.

Funny, he thought, how a Crystal Priest as powerful as Oriana Lache could have forgotten the number one rule: Trust no one.

Splinter kept his ripped trench coat for the time being, and his boots and his torn and bloodstained jeans, but he accepted a T-shirt and a grey pullover from Dr Lache. It fitted him surprisingly well. Then he followed her to the edge of the lake with only the nocturnal cries of the owls to break the silence. He shuddered at the thought of their beating wings and their wrinkled, taloned feet.

Alone, he entered the lake chamber and alone he left it, with the Omnicon secreted within the portable vortex, inside his coat. He had to be sure that his access to the Book of All Things continued, with or without Dr Lache's assistance. There was no knowing what might happen to the doctor in the coming hours. It would have been a tragedy for the book to have been lost forever within the spin symmetry of the lake.

Only after he had secured the Omnicon in his possession did Splinter present Oriana Lache with the ring. She held it in her outstretched palm tenderly.

'You see the things I can do for you?' Splinter said.

'Yes, yes I do, Thorne,' replied Oriana, breathlessly.

Almost modestly, she removed her own nexal and placed it on a bookshelf saying, 'You won't take it, will you, Thorne?'

'I promise,' said Splinter, whose promises were solid as air. He watched Dr Lache slide the supposed nexal onto her finger and knew that she was testing it out. Fenley Ravillious had told him not to worry about what the doctor thought of the ring, but this was precisely what Splinter was worried about. However, when Dr Lache motioned to the window, the glass bent inwards in a bubble, dissolving in a spray of green light, and when she pointed into the blackness outside, Splinter found himself standing in the reeds, by the lake.

Of course the ring worked. But it worked because Fenley Ravillious was feeding it by his own power. Splinter realised this, but Dr Lache would have had no idea.

'Very funny,' he shouted, his voice dying in the trees.

Then he was back in the room and Dr Lache was fastening her nexal back around her delicate neck. She beamed at Splinter.

'Thorne, you are amazing,' she said, and Splinter blushed back. 'Now, you must take me there.'

'Can't you just transport us or something?' he asked.

Oriana Lache shook her head. 'No. I need you to guide me. We must approach Ravillious's house with caution. There's no guarantee his link with it depends upon this.' She held up the fake nexal. 'It would be unwise to leap straight in. On foot will be safest.'

'Of course,' agreed Splinter, astounded by the enormity of the mistake she was making, and committing this new piece of learning to memory: that even the mighty are fallible. But to his surprise, he realised that he didn't enjoy watching Oriana make this mistake.

They didn't leave immediately. Oriana Lache spent a little time walking through her house thoughtfully. Her fingers trailed over familiar objects and she gazed through the windows even though outside it was dark.

'Boulevant would have liked to be here for this,' she sighed. 'Whatever happened to Boulevant?' Her eyes closed briefly.

As far as Splinter could see, Boulevant had given it long legs after the attempt on Splinter's life, because he could see how lively things were getting. Still, it had seemed to leave Dr Lache very alone. He watched her now, with an irritating unease that she was saying goodbye without realising it: irritating because it made him feel uncomfortable, as if he was doing something wrong.

They drove in Dr Lache's jeep, a swollen silence between them; Dr Lache contemplating what she would do once she found Fenley Ravillious; Splinter holding back thoughts of what Fenley Ravillious would do once Oriana Lache was near to him.

Whatever happens, whatever comes towards you, you must not let her turn back.

He looked sidelong at Dr Lache's profile: the prim hair, smooth forehead, fine lips, neat chin. Whatever she was, he actually liked her, a little, and to his astonishment, Splinter realised that she actually liked him.

She trusts you, Thorne.

It was a new experience for Splinter, being with a person like Dr Lache, who liked him. Who trusted him. It would have been good to hang onto that. But he couldn't. Splinter gritted his teeth, jaw muscles clenching. Whatever was about to happen *had* to happen if the King of Rats was to advance his vast ambitions. And anyway, he knew what Dr Lache really was, how evil she was. Whatever happened next, she deserved it. So he ignored the way his stomach felt like it was dissolving, he ignored the sharp taste of sick at the back of his mouth, he ignored the pull to keep looking at her face and he stared out of the window at the silent pine trees which flashed passed.

They entered the city on the western flyovers, speeding between giddy rectangles of skyscrapers dotted with lit windows where security guards kept watch, executives worked too hard or insomniacs roamed the wilderness of the early hours. They saw other vehicles, in the city there were always other vehicles, but nothing like the rivers of shimmering metal that would fill the roads by daybreak. Taxi cabs, lorries, the occasional car with a lonely driver ghosted alongside them before taking a different route into the night.

Dr Lache descended to the main riverside highway, heading for the western docks. The neon streetlamps came in pulses of orange or silver, a steady rhythm until the jeep pulled up where a row of mesh fence panels marked the boundary between the edge of the docks and the start of the Wreckage.

'Here?' checked Dr Lache.

'Here,' nodded Splinter, recognising the spot where he had set off for Ravillious's house, two mornings before. They got out of the jeep, doors slamming behind them like hammer blows in the pre-dawn stillness.

Further down the dock road the hulks of cranes, winches and container stacks brooded in massive silence, darker than the glowing sky. Splinter turned his back on them to face the emptiness of the Wreckage.

'This way,' he said, returning to the gaping hole in the mesh through which he had previously climbed.

This time there was no need for the compass. Splinter remembered the way, even in the dark, and to his left a dusting of milk-grey lightened the eastern horizon, so he knew he was keeping due south. Oriana Lache had put on a pair of soft, flat-soled boots and a long black coat and she followed him without speaking. With Splinter in the lead they picked their way across the heaps of rubble, their figures stooped as they progressed across the vast junk-pan.

The whole sky was a smoke-pink by the time that Splinter stopped and pointed. 'There. That's it.'

Oriana Lache stopped alongside him and frowned. The gaunt superstructure of the house reared up at a drunken angle, its bare pillars hard against the vacant sky of early morning.

'It looks like a ruin,' she observed. 'Or a derelict.'

'Not everything that looks like a derelict *is* a derelict,' responded Splinter sagely, forgetting how irritating he found that turn of phrase when it came out of Ethel's mouth. 'Come on. Let's keep going.' He set off and heard Dr Lache tramping over the bed of broken cement, behind him.

At about the same time that he observed a dark smudge gathering above the house, Splinter heard Oriana Lache gasp loudly and then cry out.

'What!' Splinter was startled.

'It's gone.' The doctor's face was aghast. 'My necklace. It's gone.'

Her neck was bare, although her fingers were scrabbling

at it as if they might find the missing jewellery beneath the skin.

Splinter knew at once what must have happened. The ring on Dr Lache's finger might not have been Ravillious's nexal but it was linked to him closely enough to let his power flow through it. That was how Dr Lache had been able to use it to transport Splinter earlier, and that would have been how Fenley Ravillious had been able to steal the doctor's nexal without her knowing. Until it was too late.

The small cloud above the house was darkening. Splinter thought that he could hear a distant screech, so faint it could be mistaken for rusty fence wire creaking in the wind.

'We should turn back. We should look for it.' Oriana Lache had already started to retrace her steps.

'No,' shouted Splinter, so abruptly that Dr Lache stumbled. He lowered his voice, became persuasive. 'There isn't time. Ravillious is weak and alone *now*. We have to keep going.' Then, hitting on a more attractive lie, he added, 'Maybe this is what happens when you have more than one nexal. Maybe the Inquisitors take one back, somehow. Maybe one nexal is considered enough.'

'You think so?'

'It's a possibility,' ventured Splinter, trying not to sound desperate. He had to stop Oriana Lache from walking away. 'And anyway, you still have Ravillious's nexal and he doesn't have one at all.'

Come *on*, he said to himself as Dr Lache turned around and approached him. That's it, come on.

'You're right.' Dr Lache wiped the back of her hand against

her nose which was ruddy in the cool air of dawn. 'We've got to keep going.'

'Yes. We keep going.'

She was watching where she put her feet, picking a careful path through the boulders that had once been buildings. She didn't look up. She didn't see the patch of black that had peeled away from the gaping top storey of the house and was coming towards them. She didn't even notice the keen shrieks or grackle cries that hung on the edge of the wasteland's silence.

'Once we have finished Ravillious,' Oriana Lache said, planning as precisely as she was walking, 'I shall request a meeting with the Inquisitors. With Ravillious gone, I do not see who else they could choose to complete their number.'

You could never be an Inquisitor, thought Splinter. Never.

'What's that, Thorne?' Oriana Lache was pointing at the sky. 'What kind of cloud is that?'

'Come on,' insisted Splinter, as if Oriana Lache had focused on a matter of extreme irrelevance.

'No,' and this time her voice was sharp. 'Look. What is it?'

'Smoke?' suggested Splinter.

It was obviously not smoke.

Oriana Lache fixed him with eyes that were hot with fury, but hot also with something else. Surprise? Fear?

Betrayal.

'Why have you brought me here, Thorne?'

'Can't you use your power? To see what it is?'

'No,' swallowed Dr Lache. 'I've tried. There is no power, Thorne.' She pulled the ring from her finger. 'There is no power in this. Not now.' And then the composure cracked completely. 'What have you given me, Thorne?' she screamed. 'What have you done?'

Splinter didn't know whether he was excited or frightened by what was happening, by the way that Ravillious had played his hand so perfectly.

By now there could be no mistaking the screams of the metalbacks that were hurtling towards them. He shut his eyes to steady his fraught nerves against the images that came with the screams. The dark room. The wings. The claws. The beaks.

Oriana Lache looked about, desperate to find cover. 'We have to get away. We have to hide.' She kept on saying this, and brushing away her hair, which had come undone. 'Thorne, what do we do? What do we do?' She looked up at the screaming wedge that was axing down from the sky.

Splinter stood statue-still, a gust of wind catching the tatters of his brown leather coat which danced round his thin legs. There was nothing they could do. Death was coming, but with a confidence that did not come from the Codex, he knew that this death was not for him. He knew that Ravillious wanted him alive, although he didn't know why.

A cold wind blew in his face and he blinked away tears. 'I wish I could help you, Oriana. I really do.' And he meant it. He wanted power, but he didn't want this. He thought of how Oriana Lache had tended his wounds with her own skill, how she liked him. How she trusted him.

'No!' she screamed, 'No!' before the wings crashed down and the beaks and claws fastened to her body.

Splinter dived to the floor and screwed up his eyes so he couldn't see the metalbacks' butchery, only metres away. He rammed his fists into his ears but there was no need because Dr Lache's screams were lost within the shrieking birds that covered her fallen body. When he took his hands away, the only sound was the gristle-rip of flesh being stripped from bone. Even after he heard the beat of wings and felt the air stir as the killing birds took flight, he remained curled on the ground, facing away from whatever was lying beside him, bewildered by the hot tears in his eyes.

Splinter remained like that until he saw a pair of black, shiny shoes by his head. Then a necklace dangled in front of his eyes.

'Thank you for this, Thorne,' crooned Fenley Ravillious, standing again. 'Now get up. Squirming in the dust may be your natural condition, but we have work to do.'

CHAPTER 11

When Splinter lived at the wharf with Box and Chess, there was a game they used to play with the other street rats. At the westernmost edge of the wharf, near the docks, was a series of cranes that were used for lowering dredgers into the river. They were not particularly tall cranes, but when Splinter had been a very young street rat, they looked gigantic. Sometimes, when the cranes were at work, he and the others would scurry up the metal rungs and hang from the scaffold arms over the river. The challenge was to see who could stay hanging on the longest. The temptation was to let go, before the crane arm climbed too high or the strain on their scrawny arms grew too fierce to bear. They had been sure that if you lost your grip at the top, the fall would kill you. Chess and Hex and Lynch and Jerky always let go before Splinter, Box or Pacer. Then, one by one, *they* would have to let go because of the pain or because of the height. No one ever held on to the top.

It was a bit like that now, brooded Splinter, as the limousine sped towards the centre of the city. Except that now he was on his own. And this time, he had to hang on to the very top.

There was no way of letting go. Not that Splinter wanted to let go. He had planned this meticulously and he wanted to get to the top. But getting there was hard and he had run out of tricks. All he could do now was to wait, snakelike, for any opportunity to advance his position. But Fenley Ravillious was so sly, so watchful, so powerful that there had been no opportunity. Getting higher had looked impossible: until Splinter had found the gun.

Splinter had found the gun, a small, silver revolver, inside the drawer of Ravillious's desk in the chairman's office on the tenth floor of the CREX tower. Like air, Splinter's curious fingers inevitably found their way into every space and cavity available to them, and when he had been in the office a couple of days before, they had spidered into the drawer and there it was.

But if he was to go through with this, it would depend upon the ruthless element of Splinter's ruthless brilliance. Recalling how brutally Ravillious had dealt with Oriana Lache made this easier. In fact, it made it feel right.

For nearly two weeks, Ravillious had had Splinter in his company. Wherever he went, he took Splinter, saying very little but keeping him near at all times until Splinter felt like one of the Crystal Priest's possessions. Most of the time, Ravillious acted as if Splinter wasn't even there. He hadn't offered him a change of clothes and Splinter hadn't asked. He preferred to keep hold of his tattered trench coat with its hidden pockets and their mysterious contents.

Ravillious did go so far as to tell Splinter that he was

securing the support of the other priests before offering himself to their masters, the Inquisitors, as a successor to Behrens. But he would say no more than that, and Splinter had the wit not to reveal his great interest in these machinations.

More than anything, he was struck by the ordinariness of Ravillious's life. The house was extraordinary and the hours Ravillious lavished upon his metalbacks were as ghoulish as they were bizarre, but otherwise it was a life so tranquil, so modest, as to verge on being dull. Ravillious used the telephone or computer to contact others, he ate normal food, plain food in fact, and whilst they did shift through space to cross the Wreckage, when they travelled about the city it was by car, although Splinter was gratified to discover that for this Ravillious used a black limousine driven by a chauffeur.

Splinter decided that when it came to failing to use his powers, Ravillious was as bad as Ethel. Except that Ravillious really *was* powerful; he had demonstrated that. The old crone had a few tricks but apart from them she was useless. Nevertheless, mostly Ravillious's was a life of business meetings, loneliness and static contemplation.

When I'm in charge, thought Splinter, there's going to be a lot more activity.

The only time that Fenley Ravillious became animated was in the presence of his daughter. Splinter couldn't see what delight could possibly be derived from such a morose freak. Her vein-mottled skull face and scraggy hair and her empty, unblinking eyes made him want to punch her, just to ruffle her corpse-like calm, and want to hide from her at the same time.

There had been one occasion when Ravillious had stroked his daughter's face, run his hand over the livid, waxy patch that scarred its right side and murmured dolefully in her ear. Then both of them had turned their eyes on Splinter in a way that made him think it was feeding time for the metalbacks. Tethys came and went as she wished. Splinter preferred it when she went, but this morning she had visited, stepping unusually quickly across the plain chamber where he was eating a lunch of bread and cheese with Ravillious, and the following exchange took place:

'Keppler is dead.' Tethys, purple-eyed and cold.

'A Jericho bean?'

Tethys nodded.

Ravillious leant back, breathed deep through his nose. 'Well done. There is nothing to stop us now.'

'We can go to them, Father?'

Ravillious shook his head and smoothed back his steely hair. 'Not immediately. There is some business to tidy up tonight. Then we shall go.' He looked at Splinter. 'At last we shall see how useful you are willing to be.'

Splinter didn't like the sound of that, so that was when he decided that what had been only a wild, unlikely idea until then, would have to become his next step.

On Thursday nights, Ravillious worked in his office, alone, save for keeping Splinter with him. That would be the time to use the gun. And there could be no talk, no negotiation, no hesitation. It had to be sudden and definite. No chance for even a moment's reaction.

BANG.

Then he would take Ravillious's nexal and collect Dr Lache's, from where it had been placed inside the cryogenic container under the workbench back at Ravillous's house, and then he would find the Inquisitors with the proof that amongst the humans, there was none more ruthless and none more brilliant than the King of Rats. Behrens's place would be his. But he would have to strike very fast.

BANG BANG.

'What are you plotting, Thorne?' Ravillious sat opposite him in the back of the limousine, his face grey in the evening light as the chauffeur drove them towards the Cones.

'I'm not plotting,' said Splinter, who was an expert at concealing guilt, 'I'm thinking.'

'Do you know how a Jericho bean works, Thorne?'

As a topic of conversation, Splinter didn't think this was a very promising one. He shook his head.

Ravillious slipped a hand into his jacket pocket and produced a gold and black enamelled pill-box. When he took off the lid, he held it out for Splinter to look inside.

'Looks like a coffee bean, doesn't it?' purred Ravillious.

Splinter nodded. It looked exactly like a coffee bean. It even smelt like one. He sat back with a squeak of the upholstery. Ravillious snapped shut the box.

'It is very clever.' Ravillious gave the box a little rattle and he tucked it back in his pocket, crossing one leg over the other. 'The cells within your body possess micro-units designed by nature to destroy waste material within the cells themselves. These micro-units, lysosomes and peroxisomes are contained in something called a suicide bag. Do you know why it's called a suicide bag, Thorne?'

'Because the contents could kill the cell itself?'

'Yes. Very good.' Ravillious cracked a smile. 'Once inside the body, a Jericho bean works as a catalyst, accelerating the activity of the contents of the billions of suicide bags and turning them on the cells throughout the entire body. The cells actually begin to digest themselves.'

'It must be painful,' observed Splinter, without much enthusiasm.

'I have no doubt that it must be extraordinarily painful,' said Ravillious, lugubriously. 'And it is very fast. Once the bean has been ingested, the body will digest itself within the minute, leaving nothing more than a puddle of pus. And the teeth.'

Ravillious observed Splinter with gunfighter coolness. Splinter judged it safest to say nothing as he absorbed this information and recalled what he had mistaken for a puddle of cat vomit in Dr Lache's pantry.

'How do you get someone to eat it?' he asked after an awkward silence.

'Grind it and mix it with their coffee,' suggested Ravillious. 'Mix it with chocolate. Cover it with chocolate. Slip it whole or as a powder in anything they might eat or drink. Although it looks and smells like a coffee bean, it is, in fact, without taste.' Ravillious held Splinter in his reptilian stare. 'Be careful, Thorne. If you bite a coffee bean with no taste, you can be sure that within seconds your body will start to dissolve.'

'Thank you for letting me know that, sir,' replied

Splinter, as nonchalantly as he could manage. He wasn't sure why Ravillious had chosen to tell him about Jericho beans. Maybe it was to unnerve him; to keep him under control at this crucial stage, by letting him know that there were horrible things which could be used upon him but about which he knew nothing; to keep him on his toes.

But what occupied his thoughts was the mess on the pantry floor. The only people in Dr Lache's house at that time were Dr Lache, Splinter and Boulevant. There was no one else there to be killed by a Jericho bean. So whose remains had he found?

The limousine nosed on to the plaza and swished up to the entrance of the CREX tower. This tower, and the other five Cones, were the tallest buildings in the city. Even now, their tapering upper storeys were burnished pink with the evening's last light, whilst night had drawn a line across the rest of the city. With his face against the car window, Splinter could look up and see the huge letter C with the three sharp stars at its centre, spanning twenty floors on the front of the CREX building: the same symbol that was engraved in miniature on Ravillious's nexal.

Ravillious exited the car and in silence, Splinter followed. Then began the round of 'Good evening, Mr Ravillious', 'Good evening, Mr Ravillious', as they passed through the glass entrance doors, through the foyer, into the lift and up to the tenth floor. The staff and security guards were so obsequious they didn't even raise their eyebrows at the tatty, lanky vagabond who followed in the chairman's wake, limping slightly.

None of you know who I am, Splinter thought to himself. But you will all know, soon.

Soon.

But he would have to act fast.

BANG.

Ravillious closed the door to his office. He waved Splinter towards an armchair as he rounded his walnut desk to sit at the computer.

'We won't be here long, Thorne,' he said as his high, leather desk chair accommodated his polished form with a creak. 'There are the usual Thursday night contacts to be made and a handful of unusual tasks to allot, matters to wind up. Half an hour is all it will take. Then you and I will have business of our own to attend to.'

Not if I have my way, thought Splinter. The only business to attend to in here will be the mopping up. But that all depended on his being able to get to the drawer where the gun was, and right now, that drawer was shielded by Ravillious's body. Unless Ravillious moved away from the desk, Splinter would be going nowhere and doing nothing that Fenley Ravillious didn't dictate. And given that the chairman only planned to stay here for thirty minutes, time was already short.

Then again, for months and months, Splinter had felt that he was fighting against time as much as he had been fighting against the formidable powers that were ranged against him.

When I am in charge, he thought, I shall spend a good deal of time doing nothing, to compensate for all the hard work now. Maybe that was why a Crystal Priest like

Ravillious led such a dull life: because he was recovering from the effort it took to get to where he was.

Splinter shook his head, rubbed his eyes and jostled himself in the armchair. This was no time to let his thoughts drift.

'Not much longer,' murmured Ravillious, mistaking Splinter's agitation for boredom. He didn't move his face from the screen which illuminated it a very pale blue. His hair gleamed in the desk lamp which was the only light on in the office.

From the shadow of the armchair, Splinter waited for his opportunity but it showed no sign of materialising. He realised that for the first time, events were about to move beyond his control entirely.

Splinter's mind began to work furiously, processing different strategies. Maybe it would be better to get away from Ravillious now; if he waited until Ravillious had made his move there would be nowhere for Splinter to go. But he could hardly get up and walk out; the Crystal Priest hadn't kept him within reach for so long without a good reason. He wasn't going to let him walk out now. But still, Ravillious hadn't said exactly what use he had for Splinter, and now that time was running out so quickly, Splinter's mind became mired in thoughts of what that use might be. Maybe he was to be a gift, a gift to the Inquisitors, although why he should be so desirable a gift was hard to see ... unless word of his ruthless brilliance had already spread.

Splinter gulped drily. Perhaps it was his brain they were after. It *was* a marvellous brain. Perhaps the Twisted Symmetry wanted to *use* his brain. He pictured the bare, fibrous neural networks upon which Fenley Ravillious lavished such attention and gulped again. Perhaps the King of Rats was to be stripped down to his nervous system for the purpose of neural sculpting.

That was it! The Symmetry knew how special he was. They needed his brain. And on that point, Splinter could only agree with them. However, if they wanted his brain, it would have to be with the rest of himself attached. The King of Rats was not going to be reduced to a string of nerves and frozen in nitrogen for the benefit of Fenley Ravillious.

The time had come for action.

'What is so interesting?' enquired the Crystal Priest as his tanned hands worked at the keyboard. He didn't turn to look at Splinter whose pinched, ragged form had drifted to the shadow behind his shoulder.

'Just going to look at the view. At the city.' The office was huge and the windows ran all along the outer wall. They were full of night and the lights of the city; the office blocks; the traffic packed on the sky-high grid of highways and flyovers; the flickering, strobing, luminous advertising screens with letters as tall as radio masts and faces the size of parking lots; the floodlights in the stadia; the searchlights on the rooftops; the red flashing beacons that warned aircraft where not to fly; the streams of aircraft themselves; and, far south of here, gouts of flame from steel chimneys in the factory sector and finally, beyond that, the empty blackness of the Wreckage.

'Will you come back to look at all of this, after tonight?' asked Splinter, still at Ravillious's shoulder.

'I have finished here.' At that lapidary utterance, the keys

-[173]-

were struck hard twice, the chair pushed back and Ravillious stood. Splinter remained facing the window but his feet stayed where they were, an arm's length from the desk. From the drawer.

'So it is goodbye to all of this, sir?' He nodded towards the world on the other side of the glass.

Fenley Ravillious straightened his cuffs, tweaking the silvery links, then crossed his hands behind his back.

Go on, go on, urged Splinter, inside his head.

And, of course, Ravillious did go on, stepping past Splinter and up to the long panel of windows. After all, at a moment like this, what mighty, megalomaniacal human could resist a soliloquy? Even a Crystal Priest as focused, as austere as Fenley Ravillious would wish to savour the occasion. Splinter understood these things.

'I have been alive for a very long time, Thorne,' Ravillious smoothed a hand through his well-groomed hair, 'and as the years have turned into centuries, do you know what I feel most, for all the people out there? And the billions who have died before them?'

'No, sir.' Splinter's hand reaching backwards, towards the drawer, shielded by his body.

'Pity.' Fenley Ravillious sighed. 'Pity that they know so little. They say that ignorance is bliss, don't they, Thorne?'

'They do, sir.' Fingers on the handle of the drawer, pulling gently, ever so gently.

'You know why they say that?'

'Not exactly.' Splinter could see their reflections in the window, superimposed over the city. But the reflection didn't reveal how his hand slipped into the drawer like an eel.

'They say it to keep the ignorant blissful.' Ravillious shook his seigniorial head with a gentle laugh. 'The truth is that ignorance is death.'

'And knowledge is life, sir?' Splinter spoke loudly to distract from any noise made by his fingers as they delicately scuttled over a slim notebook and found their way to the cold metal of the pistol grip.

'Obviously,' murmured Fenley Ravillious. He shrugged, his suit shoulders rising and falling with a light rustle of fabric. 'I have no feeling for this city, this world. I ceased to live in it centuries ago. I am here because I have been waiting.'

'For what, sir?' Splinter felt his pulse throbbing in his neck and his mouth was dry. Suddenly his arm felt weak, feeble, as if he wouldn't be able to pull the gun from the drawer. He took a deep breath and started to count to three. At three he would whip out the gun, put it to the back of the Crystal Priest's head and pull the trigger.

BANG.

That was all it would take.

'For the end, Thorne. A release into pure existence, and nothing else. Believe me, nothing could be more blissful. The fifth node is only months away.'

Ravillious laughed very softly. 'Thorne, it is goodbye to *everything*.'

NOW.

Splinter's heart hammered. The pistol was out, thrust hard into the back of the Crystal Priest's skull. No time to talk, no time to think, no time to react.

Splinter pulled the trigger.

Click.

Splinter didn't get another chance to fire. The blast of energy threw him off his feet and backwards, over the desk, smashing the computer to the floor. He rolled onto his side, groaning, but was too stunned to get up.

Fenley Ravillious remained looking out of the window.

'Never trust a thief,' he admonished himself, and he shook his head. 'You were close, I have to admit that.' He even allowed himself a dry laugh. 'No one has ever come that close to finishing me off. Not even the Blood Sentinels.' He turned, retrieved the pistol from where it lay on the floor and flicked open the cylinder. Then he laughed some more. 'Unbelievable. No rounds in the chambers. There should be but they've gone. Extraordinary.'

Ravillious walked to a cabinet against the opposite wall of the room, took out a small cardboard box and began to feed the pistol with bullets. 'Someone must be looking after me,' he considered, urbane, cool, as if he hadn't just escaped having his brains blown out.

He snapped shut the weapon with a flick of his wrist. 'But they don't like you very much, do they? Splinter.'

CHAPTER 12

Splinter was as furious with himself as he was terrified of what would happen next. He had never considered the possibility that the gun was unloaded. What was the point of keeping an *unloaded* gun in your desk drawer? But now he was on the floor and over him stood the Crystal Priest, his sleek form outlined by the glow of the desk lamp, the revolver a nugget of silver at his side.

'Let's stop pretending, shall we?' Fenley Ravillious's voice was calm, sonorous. 'You stop pretending to be someone who isn't Splinter Tuesday and I shall stop pretending I don't know who you really are. And as for this silly hair ...' Ravillious's eyes glinted in the lamplight and Splinter felt something crawling across his scalp. It itched and tickled at the same time, as if his skin had been electrified. Then he realised what was causing these unusual sensations: his hair was growing. He put his hands to his head to feel hair sprouting and writhing through his fingers.

'There. That's better,' said Ravillious. 'That is the Splinter I expected.'

Splinter looked at his shoulders and saw that his hair was

twice as long as normal and that it was white again, until it became black, half-way down, where he had dyed it.

'I don't know . . .' began Splinter. Suddenly there was so much that he didn't know.

'You don't know how I knew who you were?' Ravillious laughed: a hard, drilling laugh. 'Splinter, you idiot, I am not Oriana Lache. I can't be fooled by a handful of cheap tricks and a bottle of ink. We've had our eyes on you for some time: from the moment we stumbled upon you at Dr Lache's house.'

'We?' And then Splinter thought of the burn on Tethys's face and the night he had set light to the assassin who had attacked him in his bed. But still, how had they learnt so much, just from that?

'We never expected you to be there. We had to reformulate our plans. But on reflection, you presented us with a marvellous opportunity.'

'But how did you know who I was? How did you know I was Splinter?'

Ravillious explained slowly. 'Chess, Box and Splinter. We know who you are. We've had our eyes on you all for a very long time.' He paused and then added, 'Although your brother, Box, has slipped below the radar. He appears to have vanished.'

Just hearing Box's name felt good, for a moment. He could have done with Box here, right now. Fly head might have been a moron but he was handy in situations where death was a probable outcome: situations like this. Then Splinter's eyes focused on the gun held loosely by Ravillious's hip, and his voice wavered as he spoke. 'What are you going to do?'

'What are *you* going to do, Splinter Tuesday?' came the measured reply. 'You see, you have the key to secure my place. I had expected to prove my worth by defeating my chief competitors and I've done that. But, Splinter, you can enable me to bring something else to the table. Something special.'

'I don't think I've got anything the Inquisitors could use,' protested Splinter with a modesty born of desperation. He propped himself up on an elbow.

'You're absolutely right,' agreed Ravillious. 'You're no use at all.' Then he stood over Splinter and stamped him back down with the sole of his patent leather shoe. 'But your sister is a different matter,' and for a moment, the Crystal Priest's eyes flared with a manic intensity. 'Give me Chess. Chess is what I want. Why do you think I've kept you alive these past weeks? You didn't really think I was the least bit interested in *you*, did you? You're nothing.'

Even with the flat of the Crystal Priest's shoe on his chest, and the nose of the revolver hanging directly above his face, Splinter couldn't stop himself from spitting, 'She's the one who's nothing. She's nothing without me. I'm the one who's special.'

'Wrong, Splinter. You're the one whose brains will be decorating my carpet if you don't give her to me.' Ravillious spoke as calmly as if he were describing an unremarkable financial forecast.

'And anyway,' gabbled Splinter, fear tightening as his eyes focused on the gun. 'I couldn't get her for you. I don't know where she is and if I did she wouldn't come near me. She'd never trust me. Not after all the things that have happened.'

'Ah, well,' sighed Ravillious. 'Pity. I'll just have to kill you and rely upon my own efforts to commend me to the Inquisitors.'

Splinter was in no doubt that Ravillious meant what he said. The Crystal Priest used his thumb to click back the hammer on the revolver.

'How unfortunate for you, Splinter Tuesday, that I should have this gun to hand when I haven't touched it for months and months.' The hard lines about Ravillious's mouth hardened further.

Splinter realised that he really was about to die.

'No,' he screamed.

The heel of Fenley Ravillious's shoe caught him hard on the chin as the Crystal Priest spun round, away from Splinter. Splinter tasted blood from where his teeth had closed on his lip but he rolled away and to his knees, looking at what had distracted Ravillious.

In the shadows, only metres away, there stood a girl. She was tall, with long, ebony hair cut sharp across her brow and cool sapphire eyes. She wore jeans and a red, zip-up top and, as far as Splinter could see, a rucksack and some sort of tube across her back.

Even from his desperate position on the floor, he liked the way she looked. Splinter *really* liked the way she looked.

'You?' puzzled Ravillious. 'What on earth are you doing here?'

'My name is Anna Ledward,' replied the girl, as deadpan as the man with the gun, 'and I am here to kill you.'

Ravillious actually seemed to sniff the air before saying,

'I would have expected the Committee to send a Blood Sentinel to do their work, not a girl.'

'Don't worry, Mr Ravillious,' said Anna. 'I shall make sure you are as dead as a girl can make you.'

'You've been here before,' Ravillious recalled. 'With a woman called Klinky Mallows.'

'Yes. You had her killed.'

'I see. And you're here to avenge her death, are you?' Ravillious spoke as if this was very tedious.

'I'm here because you murdered my brother.' Then the girl said his name. 'Richard Ledward.'

Ravillious hesitated a moment before saying, 'Ah, yes. The computer hacker. Prying into CREX's confidential files.' He nodded. 'I gave the termination order, you're quite correct. Drugged to death with Dream, if I remember rightly. Fooled the police, didn't it, Miss Ledward? Suicide, I think they said it was.'

'It didn't fool me,' said the girl, rock-steady.

She stood with her hands on her hips and now Splinter realised that what she wore across her back was a long Samurai sword in a black scabbard, the windings of the slim handle protruding above her right shoulder. She spoke like a jack, but no ordinary jack could be this cool with a revolver levelled three arm lengths from their head.

'Turning up where you're unwelcome must be a family trait,' Ravillious goaded her. 'Tell me, how did you get in?'

'A tear in the fabric of time, that sort of thing.' The girl's insouciance was staggering.

'Well, it's very nice to meet you again, Miss Ledward, but now it's time to die.'

'Oh, I don't think so.' The girl tossed her head. 'That gun you're holding is empty. How unfortunate for you, Fenley Ravillious, that you haven't picked your gun up for months. You see, when I and my friends last paid a visit to this office, we took the precaution of unloading it.' She shrugged. 'Sorry.'

Splinter swallowed. The gun was not as empty as the girl thought. But she was his only chance of getting out of here.

'No . . .' he began.

'Shut up,' spat Ravillious, eyes never leaving the girl but waving his free hand in the air behind his back. Splinter's body spun like a flywheel and he crashed into the wall.

Crawling to his knees and coughing, Splinter tried to catch the tall girl's eyes in his, doing his best to direct them to the small box of ammunition that sat with its lid open on the cabinet to her right. Her crystal gaze didn't blink from Ravillious. 'Send my regards to your brother, Miss Ledward,' whispered Ravillious and then he screamed and Splinter only realised that the girl had moved as fast as light after he had processed the fact that Fenley Ravillious was on his knees, scrabbling for the hand that the girl had just sliced clean from his wrist. The hand that was still holding the revolver in its dismembered grip. The hand with the finger that wore the nexal.

And then, three things happened at once: Splinter dived towards the gory lump, the girl swung her sword at Ravillious's neck and Ravillious snatched up the severed hand in his good one.

Then Splinter and the girl were in a hall with a black marble floor and a grand, steel staircase: the hall inside Ravillious's house.

'This is bad,' Splinter said.

'I thought we were doing pretty well. Thanks for letting me know about the gun, by the way. You're Splinter, aren't you? Nice scar on your face; looks new.' The girl still held the gleaming Samurai sword in her hand. She wiped the blade on a piece of Splinter's trench coat as he stood beside her. 'It's not like it's in mint condition, is it?' she said with a nod at the coat.

Splinter saw how she appraised him from head to toe.

'Hair's not what I expected, but you're every bit as scrawny as I'd imagined.' She frowned slightly. 'Nasty split lip, too. Are you OK?'

Splinter grunted. His lip didn't matter. She doesn't see my true qualities, he thought. This was a shame because he liked what he saw of hers; and Splinter knew that it was a rare thing for him to be impressed by anyone, apart from himself.

'How do you know my name?' he asked.

'I know Chess.'

'Oh.'

'Don't sound so pleased. Where are we?' The girl sheathed her sword like lightning and turned on the spot to look about the vaulting chamber.

'We're in his house,' answered Splinter. Their voices echoed so Splinter began to whisper, even though he knew that in this house the walls had ears. 'He got his nexal back, he touched it. That was enough. He's transported us.'

'Well where is he?'

Splinter laughed in a way that made the girl step away from him. 'Oh, Anna, in here he is *everywhere*.'

Anna looked about again, as if Ravillious might be hiding behind any of the white pillars.

'This house *is* him, his mind.' Splinter's giggling stopped. 'We're fighting the whole building now.'

There was a listening silence where the only sound was Splinter's and Anna's breathing. Then the air was bent by a squeal of shearing steel and a silver coil of banister lashed out at them, inches above the marble floor. They both jumped and the steel tentacle whistled beneath their feet, demolishing two of the pillars. From above came a great crack and a slab of ceiling crashed down, shattering the marble from where the two of them had dived a second before.

A haze of plaster dust drifted over them and there was silence again.

'Well,' said Anna, 'that wasn't too bad.'

The floor vanished; walls, pillars, ceiling reconstituted themselves, colours and textures changed and Splinter was falling, or so it felt. He yelled, the sensation of falling spinning his mind.

There was no impact.

One moment he was falling and the next he was kneeling on a stone floor. Around them were arched alcoves full of bottles, cobwebbed and dusty. They were in a wine cellar.

Anna turned to him and laughed. 'I could do with a drink.'

Above them a huge extractor fan turned slowly, blades thumping the air as they beat. A dull, yellow glow seemed to pulse from the stones themselves.

'This is bad; this is really bad.' Splinter could hear his voice babbling. Cobwebs, bottles, the fan blades slowly beating.

I could do with a drink.

'Stop saying that,' shouted Splinter.

'I didn't say anything,' Anna replied coldly. 'You need to get a grip.'

The fan beat thickly.

He'd expected the sea first. He hadn't expected the Codex to show death in the wrong order. What use was showing death in the wrong order?

'We're going to die,' he mumbled. 'Maybe.'

'Only if we drink too much.'

'No, you don't realise. Death looks like this.' Splinter cast his eyes about the cellar, balefully, before rummaging through his pockets in a frenzy. 'You won't get me,' he began to chant. 'You won't get me.'

Anna grabbed the lapels of Splinter's jacket and shook him. 'Calm down.'

He shoved her away and held up a tiny triangle of metal. 'Just wait. Wait,' he gibbered. 'I've got to cut myself.' The girl didn't understand how desperate this was.

'You're mad,' gasped Anna. 'Absolutely crazy.'

Splinter stabbed the point of the triangle into his wrist and then saw the mark on its face. This was just the base plate. He screamed a curse, flung the metal at a rack of bottles where it jingled into the darkness and dug in his coat pocket for another plate.

From somewhere in the passages above, beyond the beating fan, he could hear a faint noise: a shrieking noise, echoing down hundreds of metres of stone.

'They're coming,' stammered Splinter. His fingers had found a triangle.

'Who are coming?' asked Anna, bemused. 'Who?'

Splinter's crazed blue eyes blazed out from the wild mass of white and black hair and his spittle mixed with the blood that zig-zagged down his chin. 'The metalbacks. The metalbacks are coming. He's going to use us to feed his birds.' He held up the triangle. 'I have one chance to save us.' He jabbed the apex of the Codex plate into the wound he'd made already in his wrist and gasped.

Anna was sitting on the cellar floor, cross-legged. On her lap was a computer the size of a book. Splinter looked over her shoulder. It wasn't a computer; it was a Link-me.

Splinter looked up. The fan had vanished. Inside the ventilation shaft, the darkness screamed.

Splinter looked up. The fan had vanished. The mouth of the shaft was black and the shrieking was getting louder, coming closer.

He dropped the Codex plate to the floor of the cellar and automatically rubbed away the blood on his wrist although it continued to ooze out. But what he stared at were the wrinkles that webbed his wrist and criss-crossed his left hand. He pushed up the sleeve of his jacket and saw that his skin had turned papery and mottled with liver spots as far as his elbow. And his hand felt weak, as if tired after gripping a weight for too long.

'They told me that it was messy,' he jabbered. He looked up at Anna. 'The Sages said that it would cost me.' Then he looked up into the black, circular mouth of the shaft. 'But what price to avoid death? I have another hand.'

'OK,' said Anna, speaking very slowly, 'I believe you. I believe this is very bad.' She looked up, where Splinter was looking. 'The fan's vanished and something nasty's coming our way.' Then she looked at the little, blood-smeared triangle. 'And I'm not sure what that was all about, but I really hope it helped. What's it done to you? Are you alright?'

Splinter pulled his mind back to what they had to do. 'You've got a Link-me,' he stated.

'Yeah. How do you know I've got a Link-me?'

He noticed that for the first time, Anna was impressed by him. It helped him to focus. 'It doesn't matter. That Link-me is the key to keeping us alive.' Splinter spread his hands, fingers clawed. 'But how? What does it do?'

Anna's solemn eyes widened as she thought. 'This house is controlled by Ravillious's mind, right?'

'Yeah.'

'How?'

'A. I., or something.'

'Artificial Intelligence?'

'No.' Splinter corrected himself. 'I. A. Intelligent Architecture.' Splinter focused on Anna's eyes; focused on them in an attempt to cut out the noises that were getting louder. And it worked. He liked her eyes; looking into them made him want to show her what he could do. He had been smart enough to be ready for death. Now he just had to be cool enough to outwit it.

He rewound his thoughts to what Ravillious had told him when they had first met, weeks ago, and he recited this to Anna. 'The house is built out of smart particles, OK? That's programmable matter which is linked by neuroreceptors to Ravillious's brain.' He even managed a smile. 'Something like that, anyway.'

Anna nodded, serious. 'I think I know what to do.'

'We haven't got long.' Stating the obvious helped. A bit.

Anna slipped off the rucksack, pulled out the slim casement of the Link-me and powered it up. 'Do you know someone called Lemuel Sprazkin?' she asked Splinter, from where she sat on the floor.

'The Traitor!' Splinter couldn't resist a sneer. 'The last time I saw him, he'd been taken prisoner by General Saxmun Vane.'

'Really?' Anna hit the return key and fired a cool smile in Splinter's direction. 'It's time to say hello, again.'

CHAPTER 13

The tiny bead of a camera lens flashed and a tinkle of laughter was emitted by the Link-me's speaker.

'Splinter, what a pleasure. You and I have never met face to face.' There was a coo of admiration. 'What lovely hair.'

'Lemuel,' said Anna sternly, 'there's no time to chat. This is an emergency.'

'What's he doing here? I mean, in there?' As far as Splinter understood, Lemuel Sprazkin should have been suffering vengeance, not hiding inside a Link-me. 'You should be General Vane's prisoner.'

'I am sorry to disappoint you, Splinter, but I was ahead of the game, which is to say, ahead of *your* game. The General has my physical form, but when I realised that I was under surveillance, that I was at risk, I took the precaution of downloading my consciousness, or most of it, and sending it to Miss Ledward for safekeeping, for which I am most grateful. Inserted into her Link-me, I can be uploaded into reality whenever she wishes.' There was a titter of delight. 'I have become a virtual me! What's that noise?'

'Metalbacks,' said Anna. 'We're stuck in a house belonging

to Fenley Ravillious. It works by I.Λ., integrated with his mind, and according to Splinter, you can help us to stay alive.'

'Metalbacks! Fenley Ravillious! I.A!' The Link-me whistled. 'You have got yourselves into a pickle.'

The shrieking was getting so loud that Splinter was finding it difficult to hold his nerve. 'We're about to die,' he hissed.

Lemuel's voice was uncharacteristically harsh. 'Lucky for you that I want to help the lovely Miss Ledward.'

Air began to rush out of the hole in the stone roof, as if an underground train was hurtling towards them.

'I'm not the only traitor now, am I? Splinter?'

'Just get on with it,' yelled Splinter at the Link-me.

'Please, Lemuel, help us. Quickly.' Anna was still calm but her eyes were fixed on the hole above.

'Now, what have we got here?' Lemuel began to chatter to himself. 'Ah, integrated bio-switches, multi-core particles (very fancy!), magnex morph jumps . . .'

'He can access solid state via the transmitters in the Link-me,' said Anna.

'Fascinating.' Splinter was already retreating from the space immediately beneath the shaft. He was gratified to see that Anna was retreating too. They backed away together. But the air was filling with the beat of metal wings and the ear-splitting screeches were drowning out the voice that rattled, oblivious, from the Link-me on the floor.

'Tricky, to realign the neuroreceptors,' Splinter heard Lemuel say. 'Still, one mind's as good as another, and mine is usually better.'

The walls of the cellar ballooned inwards and a volley of

bottles howitzered from the wine racks at the far wall.

'Dear, dear,' crackled Lemuel's voice. 'He's fighting back.'

A stalactite stabbed out of the roof, missing the Link-me by millimetres. 'Nice to meet you again, Mr Ravillious,' said the speaker, before it was drowned out by the incoming hurricane of metalbacks.

'He's not going to do it.' Splinter couldn't see how the warp could out-programme the Crystal Priest before the metalbacks would hit them.

Wingbeats and screams whirled out of the shaft. A portcullis of stone slammed down from the roof but was met by a fist of stone from the floor, the Link-me nestling in a gap between the portcullis teeth. The walls of the cellar slammed inwards, shrinking the space beneath the shaft to the size of a telephone booth and sweeping Anna and Splinter across the floor. Then the walls raced away from them, returning to their previous dimensions.

The cellar exploded in shrieks.

'Here they come,' shouted Anna, unsheathing her sword and holding it before her with both hands.

'I win!' declared the Link-me.

Splinter crouched: better to let Anna take the full force of the metalbacks first. Then his ears felt like they had burst from the air-boom of slamming stone and the shaft crashed shut. Splinter dared to open his eyes and saw the huge, iridescent span of Archaeopteryx who must have been leading and had made it through the mouth of the shaft before it had closed, crushing the others.

Archaeopteryx reared up, wings spread, talons stretched.

And Anna stepped forwards. Splinter couldn't believe it. She actually went for the bird, her sword slashing off one foot, and then the other, before thrusting up, twisting and slicing open the metalback's underside. A black sludge of oil, blood and nervous tissue splattered to the floor and the metalback fell, wings flapping erratically against the stone before they were still.

'Nice!' Splinter uncurled from where he had been bracing himself.

'Good to see you were ready to back me up,' said Anna severely. 'At least let me use your coat to clean the blade.' She snatched a strip of leather before he could protest and drew the dirty blade through it.

'Great,' complained Splinter. 'Metalback gunk.' But he didn't really mind; he liked the feeling of Anna being near him, even if it was to wipe her sword on his clothes.

'He can't use the house any longer,' came Lemuel's voice. 'But he's still here. Somewhere.'

'Thank you, Lemuel,' said Anna.

'Very nice manners,' came the compliment from the Linkme. 'You should take note, Splinter. And very nice sword-work, Anna. I see that my recommendation as to a suitable sword master has borne lethally rich fruit.'

Splinter ignored Lemuel. He knelt down to inspect a wine bottle that had rolled to his feet. He picked it up and blew at the dust. 'I wonder if this is valuable?' Even with the shrieks of death still ringing in his ears, Splinter's nose for what might be worth lifting was at work.

'So what do we do now?' asked Anna.

Splinter watched her decisive, well-balanced movements.

He liked looking at her long black hair and her face. He liked it when she turned her eyes on him.

'We get out,' he said, standing up, wine bottle still in hand. 'As long as we stay in here, Ravillious has the advantage; he knows his own house.' He hoped that he cut a decisive figure.

'Actually, Splinter, he doesn't,' corrected Lemuel.

Splinter scowled at the Link-me. There was no need for the Traitor to sound so self-satisfied. Nobody who could be turned off by the press of a switch should sound so self-satisfied.

'In fact,' continued Lemuel, 'so long as I stay in control of this building, Fenley Ravillious is at a distinct disadvantage.'

'How long's the battery life?' asked Splinter.

'On the Link-me?' Anna responded. Splinter nodded. 'It's indefinite.'

'Yes, Splinter, indefinite,' tweeted the Link-me. 'Once I was installed, I was able to advise Miss Ledward on how to find and fit a nuclear cell.' A crackle of laughter. 'So now I can go on and on and on.'

'Not if somebody clumsily stamps on you,' warned Splinter.

'In which case,' warned Anna, 'I might clumsily chop off their leg.'

The air stirred. Anna didn't seem to notice, but Splinter did. He had spent longer in cellars and underground passages than she ever had and he noticed how air moved, where it came from, how it smelt. Things like that helped you to find your way, to know where to hide, to know when someone was coming. But for air to move, there had to be openings: sluices, shafts, vents. Here, in the cellar, there was no opening that Splinter could see, and Lemuel had closed the shaft. So why was the air moving?

'Is there a door?' Splinter barked at the Link-me.

'There is a door,' came the reply.

'Is it open or closed?'

'It's closed. Would you like me to open it for you?'

'What's wrong?' Anna asked Splinter.

He liked that. She was relying on him now, on *his* skills. When it came to using a sword, she was extraordinary, but when it came to stealth, to cunning, to being a rat, Splinter would always be king. He sniffed the air again. No smell. But something was stirring.

'Just be ready,' he advised Anna.

'Like I wasn't,' she replied, waving the sword in front of his face.

'He will have to be very fast,' tinkled Lemuel, 'to beat me.'

But Ravillious *was* very fast: as fast as Splinter knew he would be. He didn't even choose to materialise. It was sufficient for him to have space-shifted to the cellar and remain in a particle state once he got there. Just doing that got him close enough to Splinter and Anna to observe them and then transport them as he wished. To transport them away from the house that was now under the control of Lemuel Sprazkin. To transport them back to the office in the CREX tower before Lemuel could say, 'How silly of me. I didn't think of that.'

Splinter was standing next to Anna, she with her sword in hand and he with a wine bottle. In front of them loured Fenley Ravillious, stooping slightly. Splinter noticed that his immaculate suit was crumpled, his tie askew and his hair tousled. But his hand was back where it was meant to be, on the end of his wrist.

'You are much harder to kill than your brother, Miss Ledward.' Ravillious swept his unkempt fringe back from his eyes.

'Leave her alone,' Splinter was astonished to hear himself say. 'You've got everything you need, Mr Ravillious. Why not go to the Inquisitors now?' He was even more astonished to find himself stepping in front of Anna.

His astonishment ended with something that felt like a sledgehammer hitting the side of his head. The bolt of energy flung him against the side of the desk so hard his lungs seized and he had to gasp to breathe. But even if Splinter could have got to his feet, there was nothing he could have done to stop what happened next.

Blue light forked from the Crystal Priest's fingers to the tip of Anna's sword and she shrieked as the electricity coursed into the steel and up her arm. When Ravillious stopped, Anna dropped the sword and slumped to her knees.

'Now, Miss Ledward, let's be fair about this,' proposed Fenley Ravillious in a relaxed fashion. 'You wish to engage in a little hand to hand combat? Then that's what we shall do.'

Ravillious clenched his fists. His wrists elongated and the skin turned metallic grey as his fingers merged into one another, creating fists of solid metal. Out of these lumps emerged short, pointed studs.

'When I've finished,' announced Ravillious, club-arms hanging loose by his sides, 'I shall send the pulp to your family, in case the urge to come snooping is a genetic obsession.' Then he swung his right arm to one side. It hummed through the air, missing Splinter by inches and smashing the desk right across the room. The desk only stopped when it came up against the door in the far wall.

'Let's keep this a fair fight, Miss Ledward. No kicking, no gouging, and no swords.' He swept the sword away from Anna's reach with his shoe. 'Come on. On your feet.'

Splinter could see that Anna was still stunned from the electricity. However, she shook her head as Ravillious advanced and stood, legs apart, as if she was the one who was about to launch an attack. But she hadn't expected Ravillious to use a metal fist to smash the floor to her left. Her foot slipped into the gaping joists and now she was fatally off-balance.

The sword lay not far from where Splinter was spread-eagled.

Get up, he shouted to himself. Get up. Get up.

Ravillious drove his stud-fist at Anna's face. She ducked, so fast that Splinter knew her wits had returned, but with one foot jammed in the floor she was prone to the pile-driving fists. He saw himself reflected in the long windows, lying on the floor, the city night oblivious to what was happening in the chairman's office.

She needs my help.

Just thinking that made Splinter's blood burn. He heaved himself to his knees and staggered to his feet, sweeping up the long, gleaming Samurai sword in his wrinkled, weakened left hand as he did so. Anna knew how to use the sword. He had seen that when she fought she *was* the sword. He just had to get it to her.

Ravillious drew back his fist, preparing to pulverise Anna's stomach. There was no way she could dodge this blow.

'This one's on me,' said Splinter, smashing the wine bottle across the back of the Crystal Priest's head. He tossed the sword to Anna. 'Catch,' he shouted.

Anna's fist closed on the rayskin handle and she scythed the sword out of the air with a hiss of steel. As Ravillious stumbled backwards, momentarily dazed by the blow from the bottle, Anna freed her foot. Then she turned her bright blue eyes on the priest.

Electricity crackled across the Crystal Priest's fingers as Anna slashed forwards. She moved too quickly for Splinter to see. But the electric light was cut short by a razor kiss across Ravillious's throat.

Splinter was certain he saw the Crystal Priest's head begin to roll back, the neck separating from the front of the chest. But Ravillious's fists were at his throat, metal dissolving back into flesh as his fingers scrabbled at all the severed skin, muscle and bone: working at them, holding back the blood, knitting the body tissue.

Splinter knew exactly what was happening.

'He's healing himself,' he shouted to Anna.

'Really?' Anna stepped forwards, inches from where Ravillious was gurgling, blood bubbling out of his mouth and severed neck. 'Heal this.' She spun off her right leg, ramming it back with point-blank force, her foot driving square into Ravillious's chest, so hard that his body slammed back into the long windows. The Crystal Priest smashed straight through the glass, one hand reaching for the ledge of the tenth floor and the other clutching at the loose skin of his neck as he plummeted into the night.

Splinter crunched over the glass and knelt down to look out. The late-spring night was cool and a breeze caught his long hair as he leant from the edge of the office, assessing the view.

The C of the CREX emblem curved from a couple of floors below to many floors above and it glinted, hard-edged in the city lights. Ravillious's body was caught in the lowest part of the C. Between his shoulders there was nothing but a stump. Splinter could just pick out a lump in a dark, star-shaped puddle on the plaza floor below. 'Like a cracked egg,' chuckled Splinter.

'Five months, two weeks and six days.' Anna sheathed the sword and when Splinter looked at her he saw tears in her eyes. 'Goodbye, Richard.'

He turned away, hearing her breath catch as the grief came. But for him, now was a time for action. However, he let himself savour the moment first. He was a human, a fifteen-year-old boy, a street rat, and now the most powerful of the Crystal Priests was dead, leaving the way clear for him. Nobody would have thought it possible, but he had done it. He still felt an ache when he thought of Oriana Lache but he knew that he had to ignore all sentiment. This was a struggle for ultimate power; there had to be winners and there had to be losers and given what was at stake, the losers had to die.

He was a winner.

It was time to secure victory. Splinter edged along the jagged base of the window frame, the breeze flicking the remnants of his leather coat about him.

'What are you doing?' Anna's voice sounded as if it was coming from a distance, although she was standing alongside him.

'I've finished here,' said Splinter, concentrating on the drop to the bottom of the C. It was no more than five metres. A thumping from the door on the other side of the room meant that already, security were trying to get in. And there would be mayhem once the body was seen. Or the head.

'Come with me.' Suddenly, Anna's voice was intense.

Splinter did hesitate, for a couple of seconds. He liked Anna, a lot. But presented with Fenley Ravillious's death, the desire to pursue the possibilities this created was consuming.

'Chess needs you.'

That made his mind up, if there had been any doubt. 'Chess needs nothing,' he spat. 'She *is* nothing.'

'You're wrong, Splinter. Really wrong.' The shining, crystal-blue eyes caught him momentarily. 'Chess is incredible.'

'Incredible?' It was strange to hear someone like Anna call Chess incredible.

'Yes, Splinter, incredible. But she doesn't know how to be what she is. And she can't do what she has to do on her own. The way you are, you can help her. I mean, you're a lot madder than I expected, but you're smart too. Chess needs that.'

People were shouting on the other side of the door now.

'Chess wouldn't want me to help anyway,' reasoned Splinter, looking from Anna to the headless corpse and then back to Anna again. 'Not after everything that's happened.'

'You're so wrong. She wants you more than anything, Splinter,' and Splinter could see how earnest Anna was. 'She trusts you.'

'She trusts *me!*' Which just went to show how stupid his sister was. Splinter was frank enough with himself to know that there was no reason for Chess to trust him.

'She's been looking for you.' Anna held out a hand. 'Come on. I can get us out of here.'

'She *trusts* me?' Splinter pondered this, but not for long. It was vital not to be distracted, not now, not after he had come so far. Below him lay Ravillious and the nexal. Chess could not compete with that. She had made her choice to be selfish and power-obsessed a long time ago. She wasn't going to wreck all that he had worked for, now. Still, he didn't like leaving Anna.

'Goodbye, Anna,' he said, before leaping from the tenth floor.

'You idiot,' he heard her say and he really wished she hadn't.

Anna saw Splinter land beside Ravillious's dead body. Then she turned from the window. Balthazar Broom was waiting for her in the shadows of the office, wearing her father's old dinner suit, staff in hand.

'Finished?' he asked.

Anna nodded. She didn't even glance at where the door was being forced open, inch by inch.

'It was difficult,' said Balthazar, 'staying out of it. You were gone a long time.'

'The killing was hard,' said Anna, blankly, holding exhaustion and grief at bay.

'When I last looked out of the vortex, the room was empty.' Balthazar was perplexed.

'Ravillious took us on a mystery tour before bringing us back here.'

'Us?' A heavy eyebrow was raised and the moustache stroked.

'Splinter was here.'

'Splinter! He is an unusual boy. Deceptive.'

Balthazar held out a hand and wearily, Anna took it.

'He is strange,' she said. 'And a bit pathetic.' She laughed, hollowly. 'I don't think he's living in the same world as the rest of us.'

They stepped into the gap through which Anna had entered the office, Balthazar using the tesseract to guide them.

'Where was he going?' asked Balthazar Broom. The slamming open of the door and the shouting of the security guards faded behind the cold vapours of the vortex.

Anna shrugged. 'He didn't say. But he wouldn't come with me. He didn't want to help Chess. I told him that she wants him, that she trusts him.'

'Far be it from me to be critical on matters of judgement,' ruminated Balthazar, 'but I do not think that was very wise.'

'It's what I said,' stated Anna, too tired to debate the issue.

Balthazar released her hand and began to lead the way along the reaching. Anna followed his broad back, watching the way his greying ponytail swung in time with his staff.

'And what are you going to say to Chess, Anna?'

'About tonight?'

Balthazar stopped and his big eyes bulged down at her. 'About *everything*.'

'She knows that I wasn't going to involve her with Ravillious.'

'Still, she will be upset,' predicted Balthazar. 'And what about Julius? You told me that Julius wants to meet with you.'

'That's what Vladivostok Ragg said when he gave me the sword,' insisted Anna. 'He gave me the sword and said it was a gift from Julius. He said that Julius wants to meet me.' She shrugged as if nothing could be more natural, as if she didn't realise that accepting the sword from Ragg that rainy night had set her on a course which could only lead away from her old life.

Balthazar smoothed his moustache. 'I must advise you, Anna, that where Julius is concerned, Chess is peculiarly sensitive.'

'Chess is peculiarly sensitive about a lot of things,' snapped Anna.

'Nevertheless, about Julius . . .'

'There is nothing *about* Julius. Not yet. All that Vladivostok Ragg said was that Julius wanted to meet me.'

'You know why?' asked Balthazar in a way that meant he suspected why.

'I think I do,' she said. He had given her the sword, hadn't he? She guessed that Ragg and Julius and whoever else was involved with them wanted her to use it and to go on using it. And after everything that had happened, she didn't have much of a normal existence left. Ravillious was dead, Richard had been avenged and her life had been torn out of orbit. Her family didn't know what to do with her; she was no longer the person they thought she was. The only thing they shared was a rawness which hurt. Already she was thinking through what she would say to her parents when the time came to leave. Maybe it would be better to say nothing at all. Some things were impossible to explain, some goodbyes impossible to bear. Not being there would be less painful.

'You will have to tell Chess.'

'I will.'

'You don't have to, Anna, I've heard enough.' Chess was standing behind Balthazar, face pale, hands in the pockets of her leather jacket, brown eyes glistening.

'How?' was all Anna could say.

'I can do things, remember, Anna? Tricks, like hands through tables or turning back time to keep you alive. And I'm getting better at it. Finding you both here?' Chess shrugged. 'It's not much more difficult than thinking.'

'You heard us?' asked Anna, feeling angry rather than surprised now.

'Some of it.' Chess dragged a hand through her tangled hair. 'Stuff about Splinter and Julius. You know, the kind of things that really matter to me.'

Anna tried to stay cool. She could see that Chess was more upset than angry. 'I was going to tell you but I needed to end things with Ravillious first.' Gently, she added, 'We can't risk you, Chess. That's what the enemy want.'

There was a long silence as Chess fought back anger and frustration. Then she raised a hand and very lightly, she rubbed Anna's cheek where a jet of the Crystal Priest's blood had left a hair's-breadth line of crimson spots, like pin points. When Chess spoke, it was slowly as if she was thinking very carefully about what to say, but Anna knew that Chess was trying not to cry.

'What you don't understand,' Chess stammered, 'what none of you understand is that I don't care about me. I don't care about risks to me. I don't care about this stupid fight. The person I trusted more than anyone has just ... gone. Really *gone*.' She couldn't even bring herself to say Box's name. She took a deep breath. 'I just want to be with you.' She gathered herself. 'And now, OK, I find out that there are things going on that you won't even tell me about.'

'I would have,' said Anna, firmly, 'at the right time.'

'At the right time?' Chess stepped back and shook her head. She even laughed. 'At the right time? I need to see Splinter *now*, I *have* to find him.'

'And I'd have told you about him as soon as I saw you.'

'And Julius? When were you going to tell me about him?'

Anna had no answer to that.

'Everyone treats me like I'm an idiot, telling me what I can do, what I can't do.' Chess was trying not to raise her voice. 'Do you know what it feels like?'

Anna wanted to speak but she didn't know what to say. She wished, bitterly, that she'd told Chess about Julius.

'Do either of you have any idea what it feels like being me? Being stuck in this?' Chess thumped herself in the chest, fist clenched.

'Chess ...' began Balthazar.

'Don't bother, Balthazar,' snapped Chess. She cleared her throat, blinking away tears, and said, 'I've got a lot to do.'

Her nose was running and she wiped it with the back of her fist, speaking quickly, brusquely, trying to hide how much she wanted to cry. 'I've got to find Splinter. And then I've got to find the Eternal.' She wiped her nose again. 'Find it and destroy it so everything else isn't destroyed first. And all I wanted, right, all I needed was a friend.' Her voice cracked. 'I'm sorry that was too much to ask, Anna. I won't ask you any more.'

'Chess,' pleaded Anna, reaching forwards, 'you've got to understand . . .'

But Chess had vanished and the cold drift of the vortex closed across the space where she had been standing.

CHAPTER 14

Splinter prised the ring off the corpse's finger. 'Thank you, Mr Ravillious,' he whispered, as it came free. He held it up to admire it, perched like a crow on the bottom of the C.

His pulse began to race. Now he held one of the nexals. Now he was in control of one of the direct links given by the Inquisitors to their most deserving human servants. Not that Splinter regarded himself as anyone's servant, certainly not a servant of the Twisted Symmetry. Splinter was interested in power, not service.

He raised his left hand, still squatting over the Crystal Priest's corpse as if it was carrion. Up until now he had survived by his wits alone, by his unadulterated ruthless brilliance. But now he would enjoy something different. Now he would draw upon the power of the Inquisitors themselves.

Inside his head, a siren voice warned him that there was no knowing what would happen if he tried to use the nexal. But he had not come this far by listening to warning voices like that.

Splinter put on the ring.

There were no sudden changes. There were no changes

at all. He felt no bigger, no stronger, no wiser. No more powerful. His left hand still looked wasted and felt more feeble than it had that morning. What was the ring meant to do?

He studied it, on his finger, wobbling slightly on his perch. It would be a lot easier doing this if he wasn't balancing on the bottom of an enormous letter C, about thirty metres above the plaza.

There was a rush, like he was a stream of bubbles zipping through water, and instantly he was standing on the ground.

'Nice.' So thought alone was sufficient to summon the Inquisitors' power. This was so good that he began to laugh. He actually tipped his head back and let the laughter roll out. Then he saw that there were people gathering about him, maybe people who had been looking up at the body caught in the lower arm of the CREX emblem, people who were staring, mouths agape, at the smashed head between his feet.

To remain here would not be good. There were witnesses. There would be a police investigation; the crashers must be on their way. Already there were shouts from the smashed window above.

Someone gripped hold of Splinter's cuff. 'You're going nowhere,' they said.

'Get off,' shouted Splinter, throwing the man off his arm, literally. Splinter couldn't believe it; all he had done was to shake his arm, but the man who had hold of it must have gone tumbling at least five metres across the plaza.

People backed away from Splinter then, and he ran. He sprinted away from the foot of the CREX tower and across the plaza to where the wide steps ran down to the roadway. He ran by the road until he came to the first narrow alley, between a colossal department store and a fast food restaurant that was closed. Down the alley, over the bins, up a drainpipe, across to a fire escape, up the fire escape, along a window ledge, down to a wall, down the wall, almost scurrying down the vertical, relying on the least touch of friction to stop himself from falling, and all without the Inquisitors' power.

When he hit the ground he ran again: out of the alley, across the next main road and into the next back street, block-hopping away from the plaza. It was hard work, particularly with a hand which was not as strong as it had once been, but it made it impossible for anyone to follow him, unless they did so on foot. And nothing could block-hop like a street rat, even a street rat with a weakened hand.

He came to a halt four blocks away, body soaked with sweat, heart hammering, legs and arms weak. His left hand was bleeding, snagged by wire that had been coiled along the bottom of one of the fire escapes he had monkey-barred. Maybe if his hand had been stronger, he wouldn't have caught it on the wire. But this was a small price to have paid to stay alive.

The alley was thick with silence and a light, fetid mist. The heaps of rubbish bags and the foul smells meant it was a safe place to be. Splinter leant against a wall and slipped down to his haunches. If he hadn't been so out of breath he would have started to laugh again.

Why hadn't he just used the nexal? Maybe he could have

vanished: gone invisible or transported himself a mile away from the Cones. But he had chosen to run. Old habits were strong, and in the adrenalin rush of the moment, he hadn't considered all his options.

Look at what had happened in Ravillious's cellar. With all those metalbacks coming, he could have just taken out the portable vortex and hidden inside. He could certainly have tried. But his mind had jumped straight to the Codex. He had been so obsessed with the visions of death that he had thought only in terms of the Codex.

Maybe the Codex had created the very situation he was then compelled to avoid?

Splinter found that thought unsettling. But it was important he stayed cool. In future, he would remember to consider *all* his options. That was how he had succeeded in the past.

From here, his plan was straightforward.

'I shall collect your sister,' he said to the ring on his finger, referring to Dr Lache's necklace, 'and after that, I shall seek an audience with the Inquisitors.' There he would commend himself to them. Given all he had achieved, they could not fail to see how eminently he fitted the position left by Behrens.

'To be brutally honest,' Splinter admitted to himself, 'I have proved myself to be the most clever human alive.' He looked at the ring and let his thoughts linger over the necklace, the Omnicon, the portable vortex. 'And now I am the most *powerful* human alive.' The Inquisitors would be glad to welcome him. They would want him.

'In truth,' said Splinter to himself, 'I think they *need* me.'

It was hot. Splinter didn't have a calendar, didn't know the precise date, but this must have been the start of summer. He cut a shambolic figure, limping across the strip of debris that led to the gaping frontage of Ravillious's house, his coat in shreds, his jeans ripped, his boots ungainly and scuffed. The high, white sun picked out the orange-brown girder ribs and reflected brightly off cracked slabs of concrete. Already, Splinter's face was wet with sweat, his hair was sticking to his forehead: white on his head and shoulders, black where it hung over his chest and down his back.

Coming here had been as easy as thinking. He had been woken by a dog, nosing its cold snout over his face. The dog had been dismissed by a well-aimed tin can and Splinter had rolled out of the rubbish, slipped out of the alley, lifted a loaf of bread and a bottle of milk from a small store where flies buzzed aimlessly before toasting themselves on an electric fly-killer and then, refreshed, transported himself deep into the Wreckage.

He was in control now. No Crystal Priests, no Committee, no Chess. This was Splinter, going where he wanted, doing what he wanted. This was the start of his greatness.

He stood at the foot of the house and squinted up at its looming superstructure, enjoying the thought that he was here because *he* wanted to be here, and that there was no one to tell him what he had to do. He could do whatever he wanted.

His thoughts temporarily adrift in this reverie, he imagined a man, sitting on a stool to his left, and then, when he actually looked, he saw only the bare concrete slabs. Strange; it was the clearest image of a swarthy, grey-bearded man in a rough jacket with a cob-pipe clamped between his teeth. There was something in his hands but Splinter hadn't caught that. Not seeing what it was left Splinter feeling uncomfortable, as if he had had a glimpse of something significant but it had slipped from his memory, like a dream.

He frowned at the ring he now wore, and then at the sun. Which one was playing tricks on him? Was this a side-effect of the ring? Visions of old men? Splinter stared suspiciously at the empty space and then marched to the front door.

There was no need to knock. Splinter was the master now.

'Open,' he commanded, and the tall door swung inwards. Boots resounding on the cool marble floor, Splinter strode into the yawning entrance hall.

'Hello, Splinter,' said the house.

Splinter swore foully and kicked the nearest pillar.

'Temper, temper! You forgot about me, didn't you?' There was a rill of laughter, like the beads of a glass chandelier jingling.

'What do you want here, Sprazkin?' Splinter glared at the walls, the floor, the ceiling.

'It's not a matter of *wanting*, it's a matter of *being*. And right now, I'm being me, in a new incarnation.'

'You mean you've turned yourself into a house?' scoffed Splinter. 'Congratulations.'

'Splinter, Splinter,' sighed the disembodied voice of Lemuel Sprazkin, 'you are so *unimaginative*. Given the unusual nature of this building, I have succeeded in transferring myself into its sub-structure. You could say that

I have re-programmed its smart particles and turned them into even-smarter-particles.' A titter of self-appreciation. 'I can use the material of this building, the raw substance, to become whatever I want. I could even make it look as I used to: transform it into lots of little me's if I wished. Isn't *that* a delightful thought?'

'Not really.'

'I like your nexal, Splinter,' said Lemuel in a voice that didn't strike Splinter as a particularly friendly one. 'What are you going to do with it?'

'None of your business.'

'What a shame you can't have the necklace from upstairs. Then you'd have a matching pair.'

'What do you mean, I can't have the necklace from upstairs?' demanded Splinter. That was what he was here for.

'Well, I'm not sure I should say. I'm not sure it's *any of my business.*'

'Don't play games, Lemuel,' Splinter shouted at the house. 'I don't have time for games.'

'She's taken it.'

'She?' Splinter had never been impatient with a building before. He was discovering how frustrating it was; there was nothing to glower at, nothing to threaten.

'Ah, I see,' said Lemuel. 'You've forgotten about her.'

'About who?'

'About Tethys, Splinter, about Tethys,' and the words dripped from the house, venomously.

Lemuel was right, he hadn't bargained on Ravillious's freak of a daughter snatching the necklace for herself. But freak or not, she was also a Crystal Priest and if Lemuel was to be believed, she now possessed two nexals.

Splinter swore, even more foully than before.

'You have a rare vocabulary, Splinter. I wonder you don't take to writing books.'

But Splinter wasn't listening to Lemuel's goading. He was thinking through this unhappy state of events. Tethys had tried to murder him once before, and now that Splinter had helped to kill the father she loved so much, there was every chance she would be determined to finish the job.

'How do I know she took the necklace?' he asked.

Lemuel re-structured his architecture so that Splinter passed up to the high room where Ravillious had worked on his metalbacks. He was whirled over to the container of liquid nitrogen, now open and devoid of the nexal and the nitrogen. Then he was hurled down through the house, or the house hurled past him and he was back in the hall, all in the time it took for him to catch his breath.

'Satisfied?' established Lemuel. 'Tethys will be returning to this house within the hour.'

'For what?' Maybe there were items worth lifting.

'For you, Splinter. Specifically, to kill you. But I am sure that a smart young fellow such as yourself has already worked that out.'

Whatever else was to be done, Splinter knew that he had to leave, at once. He didn't want to meet Tethys without preparing for the confrontation. The thought of her vein-etched skull of a face with its big blank eyes made him shudder.

'I suppose,' murmured Lemuel, 'that I am giving you a

warning, although why I should engage in such an act of charity for *you* is inexplicable.'

Splinter surveyed the house. 'Yeah, well, thank you.'

'Not at all. It's the least I can do, for someone who betrayed me so stupendously.'

Which signalled the end of the conversation as far as Splinter was concerned. If he had had more time, he would have applied his mind to how best to burn down the house. He was a dab hand with petrol, but maybe he could call upon the Inquisitors to destroy it. Or maybe he could pass the message to General Vane that if he wanted to wring a more dramatic response from the mindless body he was torturing, he would do well to visit Fenley Ravillious's house in the Wreckage.

But there wasn't time.

The most important thing now was to get out of here. Outside the house, Splinter could decide what to do next. Standing inside what was currently the body of Lemuel Sprazkin made clear thinking impossible.

So Splinter marched out of the house.

And the Wreckage had gone.

Splinter was standing on a rough village road, lined by small cottages painted in different colours: pink, sky-blue, yellow. The windows were bow-fronted with small pieces of dimpled glass. Behind him, the road buried itself in fields. Ahead of him it ran up a low hill. Beside him sat a man on a stool. Ash from his cob-pipe flecked his beard and his thick fingers worked at a net that was spread over his lap and draped to the ground.

A net, that was what he had half-glimpsed. So the man

was a fisherman. He ignored Splinter as if Splinter wasn't there at all.

Lemuel had lied, Splinter realised.

Of course Lemuel had lied. Why would Lemuel have helped him? Splinter had betrayed the Traitor to General Vane. Now Lemuel had repaid Splinter in kind, betraying him to Tethys, who must have set up some kind of space-shift, transporting him to a place of her choosing. The shift was there when he had come to Ravillious's house.

From somewhere in his memory, Splinter dredged up a recollection of Ravillious talking about how a place could be hidden, hidden mathematically, within a contradiction. And sometimes, a contradiction like that only worked when you entered it from a particular direction. So Tethys must have relied upon Lemuel coaxing Splinter to enter it in the right direction. And readily, Lemuel had obliged.

Calmly, Splinter considered his options. 'Get me away from here: back to the city.'

But nothing happened. Splinter looked at the ring and it appeared no different. Yet it had become powerless.

For a short while, Splinter stood still as his spirit for self-preservation wrestled with a hopeless sense of inevitability. But he knew there was only one way to go. He began to follow the road, uphill, resigned to whatever was about to happen.

The way was dusty, the cottages as empty as if they were deserted and a mournful wind gusted between the low rooftops. Overhead, the sky was oyster-shell white, streaked with grey. Everything was so blank, it was like he was walking through someone else's thoughts. But his senses told him this was real enough: the brackish air, the grit road, the distant clang of a bell.

Not grit: sand.

Splinter's throat went as dry as the track that the road had become. The cottages were behind him now. He was approaching the crest of the hill, beyond which the sky glowed a luminous, sepulchral grey. He knew what he was approaching, and maybe, deep down, he had known this from when he had started walking, but he knew also that there was no way of avoiding the future, so he kept on walking.

He came to the top of the hill. He had been here before.

The track trailed into a soft, sand path that led down, between the high dunes. A grave-wind droned through the marram grass, which nodded along the arid, leached headland. The sea was flat, rippling grey and silver. Near the water's edge stood the hull of a beached rowing boat, upright like a chapel door, and beyond the boat there was a table with two wooden chairs and sitting in one of the chairs with its back towards Splinter was a figure in a black, hooded cloak.

Dully, a distant sea bell tolled.

Splinter's fingers were already scuttering inside his pocket. There were no other options. This was what the Codex had shown him. This was a view of his death, or one of his possible deaths. He took one of the two remaining triangular plates and in fingers that were already damp with sweat, pushed it into the wound on his wrist. It ached because he had cut himself here only the night before.

Only the night before! It felt like weeks ago.

Splinter winced and a dark spot of blood welled out before spilling onto the metal point.

Splinter watched himself sitting at the table. It was like he was standing opposite, standing so close to the table that he couldn't see the figure his image was facing. The Codex would show him no more than this view of himself but that didn't matter. The Codex only revealed what had to be shown to defeat death, and he knew who would be sitting opposite anyway. He just had to watch what he did, carefully. But what caught his attention first was how the skin up the right side of his neck and up to his cheek was webbed with wrinkles, as if a grey frost had spread across it. This might have been the price of life, but it filled him with a heavy sadness.

I'm only fifteen, he thought. But he imagined Diogenes saying 'You were warned.'

Then, Splinter concentrated on what the Codex was showing him. In the centre of the scrubbed, wooden table top were two dark beans. He looked closer. They looked like coffee beans. Splinter watched himself choose between the beans, poker-faced. It was a long wait before he made his choice. It was only when a hand crept forwards and into his vision, the other person reaching for the bean on the right, that he took the one on the left. Splinter couldn't see what the other person did, but he saw himself put the bean in his mouth. He bit and swallowed.

Nothing happened at first. Then he opened his mouth to

scream, his hands clutched at his throat and as his fingers sank through the skin that was already dissolving, his eyeballs began to melt.

Splinter gasped as if freezing water had been thrown in his face. He let the Codex plate fall to the ground. This could have been horrible, and painful beyond description. But he had seen what he needed to see. The Codex worked by showing him how to avoid death. So, whatever was about to happen, he had to eat the bean on his right; the one on the left was the Jericho bean.

Down by the sea, the hooded figure was waiting for him.

But first he touched the skin of his right cheek and down his neck. What should have been soft and taut was rough as old leaves and scored. He heaved a sigh and wondered how strange he would look to someone like Anna. How ugly maybe.

Splinter descended the dunes slowly. There was no need to rush this. The damage had been done and he had paid the price. It was important to stay calm now. He had managed to stay one step ahead. Whatever had happened to his face, he had bought the knowledge to live.

He would be sitting opposite Tethys. There would be two beans. The one to his right would be safe. He had seen what would happen if he ate the one on the left.

Splinter walked across the sand, barely leaving a footprint. Tethys sat, head bowed, until Splinter had taken a chair opposite. When he had done so, the hood was thrown back.

Splinter tried to stay calm as he stared at the long white

hair, dyed black half-way through, the ice-blue eyes, the narrow face and the wizened skin that stretched like old parchment down the right side of the face and neck.

'Hello, Splinter,' said Tethys.

'Hello ... Splinter,' said Splinter.

The wind groaned, bending the dull clang of the sea bell.

Tethys unfastened the front of her cloak and shook it from her shoulders. Underneath, she wore nothing; his head and face attached to her white, emaciated body, and around her neck, the filigree links of Dr Lache's necklace. But she was naked only for seconds. Then her skin rippled and coloured, brown, black, stains of blood, and suddenly she was dressed in exactly the same clothes, in exactly the same state of disarray as Splinter.

Now they were identical, down to the wrinkles on their faces, the wrinkles on their left hands and the rings that each of them wore.

Splinter's head felt as if it would burst; the Codex had revealed where death lay, but which Splinter had he been watching?

'After you killed my father, I found this in the cellar.' Tethys held up the base-plate of the Codex, before tossing it into the sand. 'So I knew that you would try to cheat me. I have had to find a way of cheating the Codex. The only way is to introduce uncertainty, for both of us.'

Before his own acid glare, Splinter was speechless.

'I hate you,' stated Tethys. 'I hated you when I first saw you at Lache's, I hate you for what you did to my face, I hate you for murdering my father.'

'How?' was all Splinter succeeded in mouthing as he

absorbed how perfectly Tethys had replicated him.

'My father made me special. He knew that the way I was born would deny me natural beauty. But I have gifts that are nothing to do with *this*.' She flicked the finger wearing the nexal. 'I have gifts from my *father*. My energy fields are not confined to my body. I can integrate them with other objects, like this.'

Tethys motioned to Splinter's left hand and even though he resisted, it moved upwards at her will. His head shook as he struggled to lower his arm but it only dropped when Tethys willed it to do so.

'And I have a basic sense of precognition.'

'Precog ... ?'

'I can see ahead of time, a little way, sometimes. But not now. To beat the Codex I have had to blind my second sight.'

'But your body?' floundered Splinter. 'How you look ... like me?'

'My body was engineered with spin symmetry. I can change.'

'Like the lake chamber,' whispered Splinter.

'The ability to change into others has been helpful. I can learn things. I can kill. My father has relied upon me to do his work and I have done so with all my heart.'

'Boulevant,' realised Splinter.

'I killed Boulevant and took his place. I was meant to kill you too, and Dr Lache, but your protector intervened. After that, we divined who you were and we changed our plans. My father thought you would be more use to us alive. But I wish we had killed you anyway. Then my father would be alive.' Splinter's eyes blinked at him without a tear but loaded with hatred.

'My protector?'

'The tall boy. He saved you on the night. That is why I have brought you here: to make sure he cannot save you again. Brought you here to keep him from you and to place our meeting beyond the power of these nexals.'

Splinter was finding it hard to think straight. His mind had been scrambled by how Tethys had tricked even the Codex, and this talk of a protector seemed unreal, except that somebody *had* come to his aid the night Tethys had tried to kill him.

But not now. Now, Tethys had him alone and she could do what she liked.

'Where are we?' asked Splinter. 'How can you hide us from the Inquisitors?'

'This place is a contradiction, constructed by me. My father told you how that works.'

Splinter nodded. 'Here and not here at the same time.'

'This is my father's science and mine too. I have built this place from a memory. From a happy time,' murmured Tethys with funereal solemnity.

'A happy time?' gawped Splinter as the bell tolled.

'I have constructed this space so that we are not only hidden from view, but hidden from *their* power, a step my father would not have risked because he *needed* them.' Tethys leant forwards slightly. 'But I am different.'

Splinter understood that even without the power of her nexal, Tethys had power of her own. By comparison, he was helpless. He wetted his dry lips. 'What do you want?'

'I love my father,' replied Tethys, 'and now he is dead.' She took a small, black and gold enamelled pill-box from where her cloak lay on the floor. It rattled. 'I am not greedy and selfish like you. I don't want the things you want. The only thing I have ever wanted, *you* have taken from me.'

'And Anna?' muttered Splinter, willing to share blame in any circumstances.

'After you, *her*,' stated Tethys. She opened the dainty box. Inside there were just two small beans. She took them out and placed them side by side in the centre of the table. 'This is between you and me. This way you even have a chance.'

Splinter stared at the beans and then at the Splinter who sat opposite him. Which of them was the Splinter the Codex had shown him? What was left and what was right? He was panicking so badly, his palms were itchy with sweat. He tried to remember the background details from the Codex, but either it had shown him none or he had been so focused on his face he had failed to notice them.

'I do not want to live and I do not want to die,' said Tethys. 'I would have liked to kill you outright, but I have had to find a way to beat the Codex. That is why I have had to create uncertainty for both of us. If I used two Jericho beans, making death certain for us both, the Codex would show you how to avoid death from either. If *I* knew which one was the Jericho bean, the Codex would have shown you that the other was safe. But by replicating you and using only one Jericho bean, I have created uncertainty. By giving you a chance to live, I can trick the Codex, even if it kills me. Knowing it was in your possession, I have had no alternative.' She pointed at the beans. 'You know that one of these is a Jericho bean, but you don't know which one it is. Neither do I. We take one each and bite and swallow.'

'This is suicide,' protested Splinter.

'Only for one of us.' Tethys looked at him, eyes dead. 'And I don't care. You have already killed me.'

Sand streamed past Splinter's legs, blown by the wind. The water lapped in soft ripples and the long grass hissed. Out at sea, the bell rang.

Which was left and which was right?

'One of us is going to die now,' said Tethys. '*Choose.*'

Splinter didn't move, he couldn't move, but he felt the muscles in his arm cramp like iron as his left hand was wrenched forwards.

'Choose *now*,' ordered Tethys, crushing Splinter's fingers with her will. 'Or do I have to *make* you?'

Without being able to stop it, Splinter's hand moved towards the beans.

CHAPTER 15

In the following seconds, Splinter's mind worked frantically. There had to be a way of using what the Codex had shown him. But Tethys had replicated him so perfectly that there was no way of knowing who it had shown. And appreciating how hopeless this was only made Splinter panic more, which made clear thought impossible.

Opposite him, Tethys was calmly raising her hand, and simultaneously raising his. If he wanted to make his own choice he had to do so now. Sweat trickled down the back of his neck.

That was it!

Splinter was terrified of what might happen next. His hands and face were clammy with sweat. But the Splinter he had been shown had been absolutely cool: not a bead of sweat on him, or her. So that had to be Tethys. Only a freak of a Crystal Priest like her could handle a situation like this so coolly.

Which meant that the bean on her right, his left, was *not* the Jericho bean.

There was no time to agonise any more. As her hand

moved, so he moved his, willingly, towards the bean on his left. He lifted it to his mouth and popped it inside, knowing what horror awaited him if he had got this wrong. Calmly, Tethys did the same.

Splinter's tongue manoeuvred the bean between his molars. He wondered whether, perhaps, there really might be two Jericho beans, whether this was Tethys's way of making sure she killed him. But like Tethys had said, there couldn't be two; the Codex showed him how to *avoid* death. He had to trust the Codex. Splinter bit down and there was a crunch. The Splinter sitting opposite did the same.

Splinter would never be able to drink coffee again. After this moment, the bitter taste would always remind him of his own face dissolving in a raw frenzy of bubbling skin and flesh. He watched Tethys, horrified, as her nose, *his* nose liquefied, running down his face and mixing with the streaming pus that had been his lips. The dark cavities of his skull were exposed before it, too, began to bubble and hiss, turning to an effervescing slime that oozed in a yellow sludge down his suppurating torso.

Whether Tethys stayed sitting because she welcomed death or because the Jericho bean acted so swiftly she didn't have time to fling herself to the ground, Splinter didn't know, and he didn't care. He had survived, but only just. He remained in his chair until he was sure he wasn't going to be sick, until his hands had stopped shaking.

Then he rose and walked round to the chair that was coated with congealed, yellow liquid. It still frothed and spat, and sticky strands dripped down its back and from its seat. But on this seat lay the silver necklace, coated with mucus, and in the sand was the ring and dotted about, like so many pearls, were Tethys's teeth.

Splinter hunted amongst the dunes until he found a stout stick. He used this to fish the necklace out of Tethys's slimy remains and he carried it like this to the sea where he rinsed it in the salt water. He did the same with the ring. Only after that did he slip on her ring, but the necklace he put in a pocket of his coat.

He stood where the slow waves broke and he listened to the wind and the bell. His eyes gazed, unfocused, at where the sea and sky met in a perfectly straight line, and he let the rhythmic stillness wash over the images that nightmared through his mind: the metalbacks feasting on Oriana Lache, Fenley Ravillious's headless corpse beneath his feet, Tethys dissolving before his eyes. It seemed incredible that he should be the one who was left.

'They all made the mistake of playing against the King of Rats,' said one of the voices in his head.

'They never had a chance, Your Majesty,' fawned another.

'I was lucky,' said Splinter, to the sea and the sky, but with a smile he added, '*and* I was brilliant.'

Then he focused his thoughts on the three nexals he carried. Whatever trick Tethys had played to prevent his ring from working, whatever science she had employed, she was no longer here to preserve it.

'I want to see you,' Splinter said to the sea and the sky, but his thoughts were of the Inquisitors. Then, yelling so hard it burnt his throat he cried, 'I want to see you.'

Sea and sky vanished.

Now there were colours and there was space, expanding,

rushing away from him in all directions. Splinter sensed that his body was motionless whilst around him, star-pierced clouds a million miles high unfurled, stretching his mind with them. It felt as if he might fall and go on falling, forever. And he felt naked, as if every eye in the universe penetrated him to his core. The vastness and the speed were too much and his mind began to slip with a scream that grew so intense it drilled every atom in his body.

With a shock that cracked his bones, reality hurtled back to dimensions he could comprehend: a floor, walls, shapes, the sharp aftertaste of vomit at the back of his throat. The floor was wooden. Splinter was kneeling on it, hair hanging down his face, ripped coat shrouding him. The light danced, yellow and orange. He looked up.

The chamber had bulbous walls, the colour of sandstone but much smoother, as if polished. Black iron sconces in the walls bore the flickering torches that smoked gently as they burnt. The smoke hung in grey coils across the low, uneven ceiling. And, in front of him, four people stood in a row. Splinter looked at each of them in turn.

There was a man in a black suit and waistcoat who wore a gold and blue tie fastened with a ruby-headed pin beneath a wing collar. His nails were sharp, his eyelashes were long and mascara-black and his blond hair was swept back from his face as if he was running into the wind.

The next was a beggar, or so he appeared to Splinter. A fat beggar. His feet and hands were bandaged, his clothes rags, his arms speckled with livid sores and the hair clung to his head in rough clumps. Beside the beggar stood a woman whose face was scored with wrinkles but her hair was a deep indigo and her eyes bright white with the needling pupils of a snake. She wore a red gown and her fingers were crabbed and mottled.

The fourth figure wore a black cowl, like a monk, with the hood hanging back between his shoulders. He looked old, like a man might look old, and his silver hair was combed neatly about his severe face. In his hands he held a silver chalice and he handed this to Splinter.

'Drink,' he said, in a weary voice.

Splinter accepted the cup and, watching the four figures over the wide rim, he put it to his lips.

'Go on. All of it.'

It smelt like wine. It looked like red wine. Splinter gulped it down, messily, wiping the red drops from his chin with the back of his hand as the cup was taken back. It tasted incredibly fine compared with the dregs that he and Box had experimented with from discarded bottles. The drink hit his belly like fire but it felt good. He was ready for this.

'I am Malbane,' said the man in the cowl. His voice was calm, patient. He indicated the woman, 'Azgor,' then the beggar, 'Snargis.'

'Veer,' said the man in the suit. He inclined his head a fraction.

Splinter felt breathless, but not with fear. This was excitement, raw excitement. He was here, at last, before the Inquisitors and they hadn't killed him or done anything unpleasant. Not yet. This was a good sign.

'For your sake,' said Malbane, 'we have taken your form, approximately.' He gave Splinter a pitying look. 'Reality can be too much.'

'I wasn't expecting it: all that space,' explained Splinter, anxious not to appear meek. He stood up, to show that he wasn't frightened. Nobody blasted him back to his knees.

'You mustn't be fooled by how we appear to you.' Malbane's voice almost seemed kind. 'These caricatures of humanity are convenient masks only. All of us are here and elsewhere, even now.'

The glow of the wine had reached Splinter's fingertips. Obviously the Inquisitors needed him. If they didn't, he wouldn't be standing here like this.

'Do you understand us, Splinter?' asked Malbane.

'Splinter,' echoed Azgor. Snargis smiled. Veer stretched his fingers with their sharp nails, and curled them again. The torches flickered.

'I don't know,' answered Splinter. 'But I can help you.'

'He can help us,' whispered Veer, and Splinter wondered whether the comment wasn't laced with a little sarcasm.

Malbane stepped around Splinter, his bare feet softly treading the wooden floorboards.

'We want to reverse the phase transition, the cataclysmic explosion that created all of this,' he said, with a small wave of his hand. 'All this mess, this pain, this desperate reduction to the slow rot of life.'

'You want to stop time so you can live forever,' said Splinter, relying on words that he had heard others use.

'Who told you that?' snapped Veer, before his head expanded so swiftly and so shapelessly that Splinter was engulfed by its amorphous mass and he was alone in a blind world of howling space.

'Veer!' snapped Malbane. 'Please.'

Splinter blinked, gasping, standing on the wooden floor again.

'Please, Splinter, do not forget what we really are,' cautioned Malbane. 'And be careful.'

Snargis yawned, revealing a slithering, beetling mass of tiny arms and bodies at the back of his throat. He closed his mouth with a smile.

'You must understand the science,' explained Malbane, like a wise and patient teacher. 'It is a question of balance. In the beginning there was perfect balance, perfect symmetry.'

Malbane opened his palm. Inches above it, almost in his grasp there appeared a luminous figure, shimmering silver, like a figure-of-eight but lying on its side. It revolved slowly. It seemed a long time ago that Balthazar had used his Omnicon to display the awlis, the figure for infinity that was the symbol of the Twisted Symmetry, but Splinter recognised it at once. Balthazar and Surapoor and even his brother and sister seemed a universe away now. Probably they were a universe away. How far he had come since then.

Malbane extended his hand, fingers towards Splinter, and Splinter felt a perfect tranquillity seep into his soul. Malbane's sagacious voice flowed smooth as the deep calm that filled him. 'This is how the world should be, Splinter, poised in a deep equilibrium.'

Splinter had never felt so at peace. He shut his eyes.

'Who can tell what broke this perfection, what instability shattered the ineffable symmetry of the universe? But the symmetry broke and in its wake, this collapse left the corruption of time and the chaos we call space.'

'Drink,' slurred Snargis, offering Splinter the chalice that had been refilled whilst his eyes had been shut.

Splinter drank, and as the wine coursed into his blood, he thought he saw the universe as a beautiful, crystalline moment, unbreathing. Then the vision vanished and left in its place a spinning sense of emptiness.

'You see what we have lost?' Malbane shook his head, dolefully.

'I see,' said Splinter, handing the chalice back to Snargis, who began to shuffle about him, much as Malbane was doing.

Suddenly, Malbane's hawk-like face was nose to nose with Splinter's. 'This is not greed. This is not evil. This is beauty.'

Splinter took a step back.

'But to reverse the damage requires colossal energy and our work has been to extract that.' Malbane put an arm about Splinter's thin shoulders and suddenly they were standing side by side on a high platform with tubular safety bars in front of them. Beneath them were miles and miles of coils, pipes, turbines and fluorescing cylinders, each about three metres in diameter and the length of a skyscraper. Immediately, Splinter was reminded of the flaming cylinder he had seen in the factory on Surapoor.

'Is this a nuclear reactor?' he asked. The wine made the words hot in his mouth. How intoxicating it was to be standing shoulder to shoulder with an Inquisitor, discussing the state of the universes.

Malbane laughed gently. 'This is a fusion belt, Splinter. This is where we process the energy we extract into a plasma-form that can be stored, ready for when the time comes to release it.'

'Energy from pain?' Splinter didn't mean to sound critical. 'Energy from children? Like on Surapoor?'

'The children are going to die anyway,' stated Malbane. 'Being converted into *this* spares them the agony of living first.'

Splinter surveyed the vast, orange-crackling fields and wondered for a moment whether being alive wasn't preferable to *this*.

'Pain is merely a by-product of existence,' continued Malbane; logical, sensible. 'We simply harvest the pain to use it in a way that will eventually put an end to pain itself.' He patted Splinter's shoulder. 'And this obsession with children, with human children?' Malbane crossed his hands behind his back. 'It is true that as a source of energy they are beyond compare, but we don't focus our efforts on them alone. Surapoor was an isolated fusion centre, convenient because of the end-point of the suck worm. But as you see, the fusion process is conducted on a much greater scale than Surapoor. And there are many more sources of energy than children. Come with me . . .'

Now they were standing on an escarpment of terracotta rock. About them rolled a cracked plain from which rose other sheer crags, and across the plain marched an ocean of an army. The soldiers wore red, barbed armour and helmets, and as they marched their outlines appeared to tear the fabric of the air about them so that it fluttered and streamed as red as the armour. Their weapons were unknown to Splinter: wires, rods, sticks ending in coils and in their belts, long, sharp hooks that were so silver-bright, just to look at them made Splinter's eyes sting.

'The Ninth Havoc Legion.' Malbane raised his voice against the thump of boots from below. 'I have slowed them so that you may have the benefit of looking.'

'Where are they going?' shouted Splinter.

'From their generator to the Velga-8B nebula cliff. Nearly three million of them.' Malbane pointed to the far edge of the plain. 'We create the legionnaires from surplus negative energy thrown out in the fusion process. We shape their form through the somatopods that generate them.'

'The Havoc Legions are Azgor's creation,' said Splinter, revealing something that he had learnt from the Omnicon.

'Correct,' said Malbane, with a nod of commendation in Splinter's direction. Splinter smiled wisely. 'They are defined by Azgor's willpower. Do you know what they do?' asked the Inquisitor.

'Not exactly,' replied Splinter. 'Not at all' would have been more accurate.

'They annihilate whatever matter they come into contact with, cancelling it out of existence. You see how they destroy the atmosphere through which they pass?'

Splinter nodded, observing how the air around each legionnaire ripped, red like strips of torn fabric in the wind.

'Ultimately, this causes the legionnaires to consume themselves, to cancel *themselves* out of existence. But they are produced in such vast numbers that they are expendable.'

'What will they do when they get to the ...' Splinter struggled to remember the Havoc Legion's destination. 'The nebula cliff? Wherever?'

'There is a level II population colonising the newest star-satellites. The legionnaires will sweep through, obliterating themselves and the population. It will cause the legionnaires no pain, but the target subjects will suffer significant anguish and we shall extract that.' Malbane stroked his chin thoughtfully. 'It is a perfect way of converting negative energy, namely the legionnaires, into positive energy, through the pain they inflict.' He raised an eyebrow. 'Perfect energy efficiency, you might say.'

Then he swept his hand as if brushing aside a gnat and the plain cleared. 'Millions pass in seconds.' He sighed. 'Already I feel the suffering.'

'Do they ever go to where I come from?' asked Splinter.

Malbane contemplated this before saying, 'Occasionally. But your world is so dense that it takes too many to accomplish work of any substance. However, there are times when they are sent for a specific purpose. But in your world they appear grey, like shadows and their sickles rip through reality so acutely they appear perfectly black. They are difficult to see, unless you look for them, or they come to cut you out of existence.'

'And the Plague Breed?' enquired Splinter.

'Not so numerous.'

Without warning, Splinter was standing on a bridge and believed he was looking down at a river of rolling sludge until he realised that they were humanoid bodies, slippery, crammed together, oozing pus as if each had just eaten a Jericho bean.

'Viruses, parasites, necrosis, contagion, infection,' recited Malbane, 'packed into these swollen, malformed bodies.' He smiled, moderately. 'Always, the problem has been speed of action. What use is a weapon in battle that takes hours or even days to work?'

'Accelerated contagion,' muttered Splinter, almost bashful, but unable to resist showing what he had learnt.

'Correct, again. Something that Snargis developed with the warps. The effect of contact with these abominates is instant. Fire alone is proof against them.'

A flare of light and a salvo of screams and Malbane pointed to the ogreish lump of sore-pocked flesh that drove the plague-infested bodies forwards like cattle. 'A Plague Marshall. Their battle cries are the only commands to which the abominates respond and the fire goads burn any who hesitate.'

The Plague Marshall was liberal with his use of the flaming goad and as he approached the bridge, the air grew sickly-sweet with the smoke of scorched flesh. The Marshall drove his troops below Splinter and the Inquisitor, his thick, waddling body streaming with grease and sweat. The smell grew so rank that Splinter gagged.

'Snargis's work,' said Malbane, 'and Snargis's will drives them on, just as Azgor's power sustains the Havoc Legions. This is a small section of the Eleventh Wave.'

'And the Dog Troopers?' Splinter swallowed air as he tried to hold the nausea at bay. But he wanted to know how the Symmetry's third army compared.

'The Dog Troopers are different.' Malbane's voice had turned markedly critical. 'Unlike the Havoc Legions or the Plague Breed, who depend upon our will, the Dog Troopers have an existence independent of us. Originally, they were engineered by the warps, but over time they have formed their own society.' Malbane said 'society' as if it were a word best handled with gloves. 'They protect the Crystal Mines, they fight the Crystal Wars and they are commanded by General Saxmun Vane.'

The tone of Malbane's voice suggested that General Vane was no source of delight to the Inquisitors, but Splinter said nothing. Just the thought of the General made the scar on his left shoulder ache and he thought that if he opened his mouth he'd be sick.

'The General must always be watched,' observed Malbane. 'For a dog he is surprisingly independent, and his loyalty is not beyond question.' And then, as if to himself, Malbane muttered, 'We still have no answer to the missing shipments of crystal: how it happened, where they went. But the commodore responsible has been dealt with.'

'Can we go?' asked Splinter. Maybe he should not have drunk so much wine, so quickly. Another minute and he would be puking over the bridge. Not that that would make much difference to the abominates.

The air cleared. They were suspended in space and about them and spreading in every direction was a labyrinth, so clear, so perfect that its geometry rang with beauty. Immediately, Splinter's unruly stomach began to settle and there returned to him some of the intense calm that he had felt when Malbane had first started talking to him.

'This is what eternity will be like.' The Inquisitor had his back to Splinter as he surveyed the infinite perfection. His grey hair covered the nape of his neck, touching the loose hood of his cowl. 'A dimension constructed entirely of amarantium. A dimension that will remain unchanging, forever, and which will be the only existence capable of surviving the vast collapse to perfect symmetry.'

'When we reach … *you* reach the fifth node?'

'Very good, Splinter, very good,' said Malbane, with his priest's smile. 'Without crystal, we would be nothing.'

They were back in the torchlit chamber and the other Inquisitors were waiting. Splinter's head ached, but it was time to stake his claim. He dug Oriana Lache's necklace out of his coat, pulled the rings from his fingers and held out the nexals in one hand.

'I have brought you these,' he said.

Malbane faced him. 'Yes.' He sounded a little disappointed. 'You have returned to us what is ours already. What is that meant to achieve?' He raised an eyebrow, quizzically. The other Inquisitors circled Splinter: Snargis to his left, Azgor to his right and Veer behind him.

Don't panic, Splinter told himself. You can do this. If they wanted to kill you, you wouldn't be standing here now and Malbane wouldn't have taken you on his guided tour of the Symmetry.

'You are one Inquisitor short.' Splinter didn't wish to sound indelicate, but there was no point in being coy.

'We are as we are,' Malbane said.

'The Crystal Priests wanted to replace Behrens,' insisted Splinter. 'And I beat them. I beat them all and that's because I was cleverer than any of them. I can be the one who takes Behrens's place.' He met Malbane's soul-searching gaze nose to nose. 'I want to join you.'

'And do what?' enquired Malbane.

Splinter's voice was hoarse. 'And be a king.'

The Inquisitor covered Splinter's proffered hand with his own. His grasp was as warm as a grasp should be, and no stronger. But with the least effort, Malbane rotated Splinter's hand and the nexals clattered to the floor.

'And what have you brought us?' The thin, stern face seemed to strip away Splinter's skin and bone and stare into his mind. 'What have you brought us, Splinter?'

'Myself,' said Splinter, who had thought that just getting this far would be enough.

'He brings us *himself*,' echoed Snargis, in mock-gratitude.

'*Himself?*' ridiculed Azgor, snake-eyed venomous.

'*Himself*,' whispered the cold voice of Veer.

Malbane turned his back on Splinter and paced across the chamber. 'I am afraid that you will have to do better than that.' He addressed the scalloped wall. 'There is no doubt that you are a human of significant ability, a human with potential. I think you have all the ingredients to be a king. But what really matters, Splinter, what counts above all else is not what we can do for you.' Malbane turned about and advanced upon Splinter, the torchlight alternately illuminating and darkening his face. 'What matters is what *you* can do for *us*.'

'For *us*,' hissed Azgor.

'You need time to think.' Malbane was patient. Solicitous, even. 'So we have constructed this place for you.'

'This cell?' asked Splinter. 'So I'm a prisoner?'

'You misunderstand,' laughed Malbane, apologetically. 'You will see that this is a castle.'

'Fit for a *king*,' added Snargis, and he bowed, revealing a knot of pink threadworms that twitched and writhed in his scalp.

'And you will not be alone.' Malbane escorted Splinter towards a low, wooden door. 'We have ensured that you have company.'

'Someone you already know,' said Veer, from behind him.

Malbane took hold of the handle but before he opened the door he asked, 'How much do you want to be a king, Splinter? How much do you want to become one of us? To achieve perfection and to live *forever?*'

Splinter didn't want to appear hesitant. 'With all my heart.'

'Good.' Malbane rationed out a smile. 'Then you must think hard about what you can do for us. Search within yourself, Splinter, and balk at nothing. It would be a terrible shame if you missed this great opportunity.'

Snargis rested a bandaged hand on Splinter's shoulder. 'If you throw away all that you have worked for.'

Veer's lips were against his ear. 'All that you deserve.'

Malbane opened the door and motioned to the person who was waiting outside. 'Introductions will be unnecessary,' he said.

CHAPTER 16

'You!' Splinter embedded his derision in laughter. 'What are *you* doing here?'

'My good luck, I suppose,' shrugged Saul. The tall boy who had helped Splinter and Chess and Box on the train in Surapoor just shrugged, but Splinter read the warning in his large, dark eyes: say no more. The large dark eyes that Chess had liked so much.

'Show him the castle,' said Malbane, disinterestedly. 'The audience chamber might be particularly encouraging. Make sure he is comfortable, Saul.' He turned to Splinter. 'We shall give you a little thinking time. Please don't disappoint us, Splinter. Don't disappoint *yourself*.'

And with that, the Inquisitors vanished, leaving the two of them in a corridor of smooth, ginger walls which bulged in a way that struck Splinter as muscular. The floor was made of perfectly flat, polished tiles and a well of daylight silvered the shallow brick steps that curved upwards like a lizard's back at the end of the passage.

'What the hell are you doing here? Why aren't you dead?' Twice now, Splinter had seen Saul on the verge of death at the hands and teeth of General Saxmun Vane: the first time in the factory on Surapoor; the second, when he and Saul had been prisoners on PURG-CT483, and Splinter had struck his bargain with the General to capture the Traitor, leaving Saul to the ravenous fury of the General.

'What's wrong with your face, Splinter?' asked Saul, frowning. 'And your hand? What happened?'

Splinter withdrew his wrinkled left hand into the cuff of his coat. 'Are you with *them*?' With his other hand he pointed into the chamber where the Inquisitors had been. Saul was a clear head taller than him, but his hand clenched into a fist.

'I know I've got some explaining to do,' hurried Saul, 'but you've got to forget everything you think you know about me.'

'What? That you're a squealer? A stooge for the Symmetry?'

Saul grasped Splinter's forearms in his hands. His long, black hair shook as he insisted, 'Just listen to me. I'm not on their side, OK?' He spoke in a whisper. 'When you saw me before, I wasn't working for them. No way.' Saul pointed to his own face. 'This nose wasn't always broken.' Splinter could see that he was right about that. When he had last left Saul, Saul had been lying on the floor and clutching his face where the General had just smashed it with his fist. Now he had a boxer's nose to match his square jaw.

'Let's walk and talk,' suggested Saul, his soft lips breaking into an understanding smile. 'I owe you an explanation and I can show you how generous your hosts have been.' He put his hands in the pockets of his jeans and strolled towards the stairwell where the daylight reflected off his white shirt.

'Obviously, I've been in the dark for too long,' muttered Splinter, rubbing his eyes as they climbed the steps. At the top they came to a spiralling brick path which followed the curved wall of a tower so that Splinter could see how it wound its way up above him. The azure sky was deep and brilliant and the air was cool. Splinter blinked as his sight adjusted to the jewel-brightness.

Immediately beside them was a deep balcony with a smoothly undulating parapet. Polychromatic tiles decorated it like smooth scales.

'Prepare yourself for a surprise,' warned Saul, as Splinter stuck his head over the edge.

Splinter swore quietly. 'Where does it go?' he gasped. He looked up and he looked down and as far as he could see, the castle went on forever: one tower encircled by an outer staircase, broken by undulating balconies like this one, extending into the sky in both directions until sandy stone and fathomless blue became one.

'Who lives here?' asked Splinter, picking out the doorways and porticos that studded the endless walls. Some looked tiny as beetle backs whilst others were huge, supported by funicular stalactite columns that gleamed a ceramic glaze, or yawned like stone-beamed caverns.

'You live here, now,' said Saul, standing behind Splinter's shoulder. 'The Inquisitors constructed this for you. They have great expectations. And they have been generous, in their own way. It is a gift, or it will be, if you give them what they want.'

Splinter pushed himself away from the balcony.

'Come on,' said Saul, mounting the stairs. 'I'll show you the audience chamber and your rooms. There's food there. And clothes.' He smiled wryly. 'I think you need both.'

Splinter remained by the steps. 'I want you to tell me what you're doing here. I want you to tell me what you've been doing all along.'

Footsteps interrupted them as a young woman in a plain dress clipped down the stairs and past them.

'Who's that?' asked Splinter, who hadn't stopped to consider whether this apparently endless castle would be home to anyone other than him.

'A scullion. A member of your staff.' Saul laughed at Splinter's momentary bewilderment. 'You don't think a place like this runs itself, do you? And you need staff.'

Splinter laughed then. Of course he had to have a staff; he was going to be a king. He looked down the stairs in the direction that the young woman had gone. She was quite a pretty young woman. Or was it the wine? The heat still lingered in his belly.

'The staff are discreet, but they turn up everywhere.' Saul lowered his voice. 'It would be better to save my explanations for when we get to your rooms.'

'The King of Rats should be kept waiting for nothing,' said a voice amongst his thoughts.

'The King of Rats would very much like to survey his domain,' said another.

'The King of Rats is not yet a king,' observed a third.

That final thought tempered Splinter's excitement. 'Well let's get moving,' he snapped at Saul. 'And don't bother talking until you're actually going to start answering my questions.'

The most surprising thing about the castle was the way in which its space on the outside didn't match its space on the inside. On the outside it looked like one, unending tower. On the inside there were more staircases, halls, lawned quadrangles, cloisters and ornate footbridges than ever looked possible from the outside. In this way it was a bit like Fenley Ravillious's house, but it was very much larger: in fact, from what Splinter had seen when he'd looked over the balcony, it looked endless. However, unlike Ravillious's house, the castle showed no signs of changing its mind about its layout. So, given time, Splinter would be able to learn his way about.

There was a sinuous, organic design to the castle that made it different from any he could have imagined. Straight lines were softened into bone-like curves, fungiform columns opened into cupolar ceilings, which curved like the insides of shells, parabolic arches throated the long corridors and wrought-iron window grilles twisted like vine leaves. And instead of dull stone, there were radiant mosaics, patterned tiles shaped like pineapple scales or fish-tails on the floor and sometimes on the walls, coloured glass in the windows, and the ceilings were made of tiny bricks in intricate polygonal designs or plaster moulded smooth and bulbous.

'The audience chamber,' was the only thing Saul said on the way to Splinter's rooms.

The audience chamber was the largest room Splinter had seen in the castle, as large as the nave of a cathedral. It had a vaulted ceiling and at the far end, a semi-circular wall in which there were carved five tall alcoves. Within each alcove, there was a throne. The thrones were gold, veined with crimson, their forms as wild as flames in motion, as if they had been torn out of fire and cooled to these solid shapes.

'Five,' whispered Splinter, as he and Saul stood in a gallery, high in one of the walls of the audience chamber. '*Five* thrones,' and his voice whispered back at him from the vaulted ceiling.

The floor was of polished, rose marble, the walls and ceilings white and beamed by dark wood which curved up to meet like fingers with tips pressed together in contemplation. Save for the thrones like tongues of fire, the vast chamber was empty.

After more climbing around the outside of the castle, they came to Splinter's apartment: three rooms consisting of a sitting room, a bathroom and a bedchamber. All of them had white plastered walls, wooden floors and low, beamed ceilings. In the sitting room there were comfortable couches and colourful rugs and wooden slatted shutters that could be opened. In the bathroom there was a lavatory and a huge ceramic tub that sat on four conch feet, and in the bedchamber, which was the biggest of the three, there were wooden wardrobes down one wall and in the centre of the floor, a large, low bed.

Splinter pushed open the shutters and leant out of the sitting room and saw that above and below, the castle extended into the summer blue without end, like a tower without roof or foundations.

'You must be hungry,' said Saul from the centre of the room.

He was right. Splinter was ravenous.

Saul was standing by a round dining table about which were set five chairs. On the table there was a silver tray bearing a whole roast chicken and a bowl of ripe tomatoes, a cutting knife, a cup and a pitcher of water. Splinter sat at the table and began to eat with the messy haste of someone who wasn't convinced the food would remain where it was long enough for him to fill his belly.

'Go on,' he spluttered through a mouthful of chicken leg. 'Explain.' He waved the chicken leg at a chair opposite.

'Just hear me out before you start interrupting,' requested Saul, dropping into the seat.

'My mouth's too busy to interrupt,' munched Splinter.

'I know about you and your brother and your sister,' began Saul, running a hand through his long hair. 'I know about the Committee, I know about Ethel, I know about the Twisted Symmetry.'

Splinter grunted. That much was obvious. He tore off the other chicken leg and began to devour it.

'It wasn't by accident that I met you on Surapoor. I was sent there to meet you; to look out for you.' Saul's large eyes looked steadily into Splinter's hungry ones. 'I was sent by Ethel.'

Splinter choked on the strip of chicken skin he was swallowing.

'Listen,' said Saul before Splinter could embark on any interruption. 'There are a lot of people who work for the Committee, Splinter. It might surprise you to learn that you don't know all of them. I was sent to shadow you and Box and Chess.' Saul shook his head. 'I didn't do a very good job.'

Splinter remembered how Saul had stepped in when some of the boys on the desert train had been about to beat up Chess. He also remembered how they had seen him interrogated by General Vane and how he had refused to tell the General anything about Chess. Splinter poured himself a cup of water, slurped it down and took a tomato.

'Go on.' The tomato exploded over his wrinkled hand as he bit into it.

'When you next saw me, I was destined for the General's food store.'

Splinter nodded, weighing all of this up. Saul might not have been eaten but he certainly had one hell of a broken nose now.

'I didn't fancy my chances in a locked room with the General, and I wanted to stick to my mission.' Saul paused, took a tomato and inspected it. 'I've worked for the Committee for a long time, Splinter. I've risked a lot and I have my reasons. When you've been through all that I have, you don't give up, *ever*.'

'So?' Splinter peeled a whole breast off the chicken. The skin was so crisp and tasty that he licked his fingers before setting his teeth into the white meat.

'So, I cut a deal with the General. I cut a deal with the Twisted Symmetry.'

Splinter chewed more slowly. 'What kind of deal?'

'I offered to work for them.'

'You became a double agent?'

Saul replaced the tomato. 'That's what I told them. I told them I could get secrets from the Committee and that I could find out about you and Box and Chess because you knew me. Because you'd all trust me.'

'Hardly,' muttered Splinter.

Saul leant forwards, intense. 'But I'm not working for them,' he whispered. 'That's just what I told them.'

'Why am I going to believe that?' asked Splinter. Saul seemed frank, but plainly the Inquisitors were content for him to be here.

'Because all the time I was meant to be working for them, I've been looking out for *you*.'

'*Me!*' laughed Splinter.

'You put yourself in grave danger, Splinter.'

'Occasionally,' admitted Splinter. His pride at defeating the Crystal Priests and placing himself so close to what he wanted almost made him choke.

'I wanted to help you.'

'How? When?'

Saul kept his voice low. 'I had never expected you'd find your way to Oriana Lache. You took some tracking down.' He laughed gently. 'But I think I arrived just in time.'

'You!' exclaimed Splinter. Now he remembered, Oriana Lache had spoken about seeing a tall figure on the far side of the lake, when they had been having breakfast. That night, Tethys would have killed him, but for the person who had entered the room and driven her out. And Tethys had said he had a protector: a tall boy.

Splinter was stunned; Saul might actually be telling the truth.

'I got you out of that room, but after that I had to lie low. It would have made things difficult if Dr Lache had found me there. I would have had a lot of explaining to do, to this lot.' Saul swung his head towards the door as if the Inquisitors might have been eavesdropping right behind it. 'And after that, I don't know where you went. I discovered Dr Lache was dead and you had vanished.'

That would be correct, Splinter realised. 'Fenley Ravillious's house is hidden by weird mathematics. I was there.'

'But then I found out Fenley Ravillious was dead and you were in the city and then you vanished, *again*.' Saul was perplexed. 'Just at the moment I was trying to get to you. I was worried to death because Tethys was coming for you, too.'

That was right. Saul wouldn't have been able to reach him because Tethys had folded them both inside a contradiction of her own. Until she had been destroyed.

'Well,' began Splinter, not wishing to reveal how impressed he was with Saul's story, 'what do you plan to do now?'

'Get you out of here, somehow.'

Splinter held up a hand. 'I don't wish to seem ungrateful,' he pointed out, 'but I have been working very hard to get *in* here.'

'But Splinter, you *can't* stay.'

'Why not?'

Saul spoke with sharp urgency. 'Because you'll become one of them ...'

'Exactly,' smiled Splinter.

'Let me finish. You'll become one of them if you do what they want.'

Splinter smiled some more; the Inquisitors had said as much.

'Splinter, listen. The Inquisitors want Chess. You give them Chess and I guarantee you will be the king you want to be. They will do anything for you.' He shook his head, long hair loose, and his eyes were pleading. 'What do you think this is all about?' He pointed to the walls around them. 'This is just a taste of what they will give you. They've given you all of this before you've done *anything* for them. I've never known them to be like this about anything else. That is how much they want Chess. And this is barely a hint of what they will give, to have her. So we need to get you out of here. Soon.'

Splinter held up his hand again. His head was too busy for any more of Saul's breathless exhortations. He felt tired and excited and anxious, all at the same time. And irritated. *Always*, things came back to Chess: who wanted her, how important she was, how *special* she was. Here he was, having defeated the most powerful, the most treacherous humans to stalk his world, having defeated them *alone*, and still the talk was Chess, Chess, Chess. But he knew also that whatever he thought of her, this had always been about Chess. And maybe, deep down, he had known for a long time that it might come to this.

Splinter understood the things people would do for power, even Inquisitors. Find what they wanted and they would give you anything. He smiled to himself; other people were so easy to use.

But to give Chess to the Twisted Symmetry? She was his sister.

'So what?' fired up a voice in his head. 'She's hardly behaved like one.'

That was true. She had been selfish, she had used him and it would be typical of her if she was the reason he *didn't* become a king. And from what Saul had just told him, there was absolutely no doubt that that was what *would* happen if he gave the Inquisitors what they most desired.

Saul's big eyes met his. They were gentle, imploring eyes. They didn't go with that broken nose at all.

Until a couple of days ago, Splinter would have believed there was an insuperable problem with any attempt by him to get close to Chess. Splinter was smart enough to know that after all that had passed between them, after the nastiness, the arguments, his threats, his anger, after he had chosen to leave her, Chess was hardly going to rely upon him for anything.

But it seemed that he was wrong about that. Chess was more stupid than he had thought. Anna had told him how Chess had been looking for him, how he was what she wanted more than anything. It was extraordinary but it was true.

Splinter cast a calculating smile at Saul. 'She *trusts* me,' he whispered.

CHAPTER 17

Even in the mornings it was dark in the bedchamber, because there were no windows. Often, when he awoke, Splinter found that his thoughts slipped back to Dr Lache, before the metalbacks, and he wondered what would have happened had he stayed with her. She had liked him. She hadn't asked anything of him by the end of their time together. He could have been very comfortable. Things could have been very easy; or so he began to think. And then, more often than not, his thoughts, these unruly, mind-of-their-own thoughts, would drift to Anna.

Anna had asked him not to go. She thought he was strange, he could tell that, but if he had stayed maybe she would have got to like him. This was an unusual thought because Splinter had never much bothered before about who liked him, not unless he wanted something from them. But he would have liked Anna to like him, just for the sake of it. It would have been good if she liked him. He really liked her. Maybe, if he had stayed ...

'Get up, Your Majesty, get up.' The voice would interrupt his thoughts, rolling Splinter out of the low, wide bed. His thin feet shuffled over the wooden floor, eyes groggy until he wandered into the sitting room where he was hit by daylight through the open shutter and the smells of breakfast. Always, breakfast would be there and it was always a breakfast fit for . . .

'A king, Your Majesty, a king cannot lie in bed, dreaming like a sentimental old widow. Now eat.'

'All right, all right,' Splinter would mutter, wrapping the brocade dressing gown about himself and collapsing into a chair. But the voice was right. It always felt much better when he ate. By the time he had consumed eggs, lamb chops, fried potatoes, toast, jam, a flagon of hot chocolate and a couple of pints of orange juice, his mind was alive.

Although he was free to go as and where he wished, Splinter had been content to spend whole days of these last couple of weeks in his sitting room, absorbed by the Omnicon. His thin face, which had grown a little less hollow from all the breakfasts, lunches, dinners and suppers he had consumed, would be illuminated by the ivory glow of knowledge. And the knowledge that Splinter sought was knowledge of kings: how they should look, how they ruled, how they were crowned.

If he was going to be a king, there had to be a proper coronation, with guests and music. He had started to plan how this should be done and after hours of research into the many varieties of coronal anointment, he had come upon the perfect musical accompaniment, an anthem of sufficient grandeur and dignity to reflect the moment.

'Zadok who?' had asked Saul on one of his many visits.

'Zadok the Priest and Nathan the Prophet,' Splinter had repeated. 'It's a coronation anthem.'

'I don't get it.' Saul was confounded.

'No, you wouldn't.'

Saul had become a nuisance, arriving at his rooms without warning, appearing during Splinter's occasional, contemplative rambles about his castle, always harping on about not agreeing to what the Inquisitors wanted, about getting away from here, about getting away before the Inquisitors came to see what Splinter could do for them.

Saul was so incessant that sometimes, Splinter would take the portable vortex, place it at the back of one of the deep wardrobes in the bedchamber and climb inside, so that no one would know where he was. The cold air was soothing, and sitting on a reaching, arms round his knees and knees up to his chin, he could think. He could plan.

Saul was so stupid. If Splinter wanted to go, he could go, at any time, to any place. He had the means and he had the knowledge. The portable vortex was the perfect escape route. Splinter didn't go because he didn't want to go.

On this particular morning he woke sprawled over the bedspread and stared into the gloom for several minutes before pushing himself out of bed and padding through the semi-darkness in search of his dressing gown. Today he would dress in the black, mandarin-collared jacket and black trousers he had taken to wearing, and a pair of long-toed black shoes. The high collar hid the skin that covered the right side of his neck like grey bark. There was no way of hiding where it crept up his face. His wardrobes had been stocked with a variety of clothes but Splinter liked clothes that were so close-fitting they became part of him, and always, he preferred black. It was a most useful colour.

But first, breakfast. He found his dressing gown on the floor where he had left it the night before, pulled it on and squinting at the day as if it was lemon juice in his eyes, he shambled into the sitting room.

'Good morning, Splinter,' said Malbane, seriously. He sat at the table. Veer, Snargis and Azgor occupied three of the other chairs. Malbane gestured to the final, empty place. 'Please,' he said. 'Join us.'

No breakfast had been provided.

Splinter's wits began to sharpen swiftly. He hadn't seen the Inquisitors since he had arrived in the castle, which must have been about two weeks ago. But they had never been far from his thoughts. He had been sure he would be ready to deal with them when the time came, but now the time had come, his mouth was dry and his stomach was churning. However, they were here because they needed him. He ignored the chair that had been indicated and strolled to the window, as coolly as he could muster in a brocade dressing gown.

'Chess, Chess, Chess,' he sighed, looking up at the eternally blue sky and sniffing.

From behind he heard an ecstatic gasping and a frenzied slithering, but when he turned round he saw four Inquisitors staring back, impassive. Splinter looked back out of the window.

'She's nothing, you know. Nothing special. I know. I'm her brother. But I know how badly *you* want her.'

'She is ... important to us,' said Malbane, carefully.

'And what about me?' snapped Splinter, facing the Inquisitors now. 'Aren't I important?'

'Splinter.' Malbane's voice was a balm, soothing blistered pride. 'We want to *use* Chess, but we want *you* to join us. How much more important can you be?'

'I want to be a king.'

Malbane's wise eyes looked about the apartment. 'You already have a castle.'

'And I want power.'

'And you shall have power, after you have helped us.'

Veer spoke, his voice urgent and raw as flayed flesh. 'But can you help us? Can you do this?'

Half of Splinter's mouth smiled, but he felt the total satisfaction when he said, 'She trusts me. She will do whatever I want.'

Azgor's crabbed hand tightened where it had been gripping the table, tearing through the wood with a crunch. Snargis opened his mouth and gasped with a worm-tailed delight, the pink, wriggling bodies vanishing as he sucked inwards.

'When?' hissed Veer. 'When can we have the girl?'

'After I've been crowned,' announced Splinter.

'Of course,' agreed Malbane, before any of the others had the opportunity to react. 'Naturally.'

Splinter had assumed the Inquisitors would bargain over his request. He was taken aback by Malbane's ready agreement. 'Really?' he gasped.

'Of course, Splinter.' Malbane rose, his black cowl swaying as he approached Splinter and placed an arm about his shoulders. He laughed, generously. 'Your head has been filled with a lot of rubbish about us, I see. We're not entirely bad, you know! You wish to be crowned as a king before we proceed with this business? Then you *shall* be so crowned.'

'I've planned it all,' gushed Splinter. 'Down to the music.'

'Good, good.' Malbane patted Splinter's back. 'That will save a lot of work and cut out disagreements. I have known there to be such arguments about coronation arrangements, who sits where, that sort of thing.'

'Will there be guests?'

'Splinter.' Malbane stepped back and looked him up and down. 'You are to be a king, you will have power and subjects to rule as you like. We already have plans for a vast sector for you to govern.'

'You do?'

'We do. Of course there will be guests at your coronation.' Malbane's severe face softened. 'You don't believe me, do you?'

'It's just ... I want ... Nobody has ever ...' Splinter clamped his mouth shut. Suddenly he felt he was about to make an idiot of himself. He swallowed back the lump in his throat and blinked the wetness out of his eyes.

'My poor, poor boy,' consoled Malbane. 'You have come so far and you have done it all on your own. But believe me, *we* understand and we know that you are here, now, because you deserve to be here.'

Splinter nodded. 'Thank you,' he choked.

Malbane patted his arm as a father might, thought Splinter, although never having known a father, he couldn't be sure.

'When?' asked Splinter, as the Inquisitor walked away.

'How about tomorrow?' volunteered Malbane, as if he were planning nothing more complex than a game of football.

'Can we be ready for then?'

'Splinter, you are with the Symmetry now. We can do whatever we want. You must get used to this.' He pulled up his hood and his ancient eyes looked out. 'You need to have a haircut, of course. Your unusual hair colour has baffled us all. But after that, we can proceed.'

As one, Veer, Snargis and Azgor stood.

'And after the coronation, Splinter, you and I will talk about Chess, and how best to acquire her. You understand?'

Splinter was still trying to absorb the speed at which everything was happening. 'Yes, yes, I understand. Of course. And thank you.'

Malbane raised a hand and shook his hooded head. No thanks were necessary.

Splinter blinked and when he next looked, the Inquisitors had gone. But there was a banging on the door.

'What?' snapped Splinter, after he had drawn the bolts and let Saul in.

'What was happening?' demanded Saul. 'The door was locked. You never lock the door.'

Splinter hadn't locked the door on this occasion, but he didn't say that to Saul. It was good to see him sweating. Saul's self-assurance, his comings and goings had been very irksome. Now it was Splinter who was in control and Saul who was wrong-footed.

Splinter enjoyed telling him about the Inquisitors' visit and the plans for the coronation.

'They don't trust me,' Saul kept saying. 'They would have let me be here if they did. Did they mention me? Did they say anything about the Committee?'

Splinter pondered this a long time before saying, 'Not that I recall.'

Saul released a sigh like a pressure-cooker. 'Thank goodness.' He laughed anxiously. 'So we still have a chance to get you out.' When Splinter said nothing to that, Saul looked up through the black fringe that hung over his black eyes and asked, 'What about Chess?'

'What *about* Chess?' responded Splinter.

'Tell me you haven't agreed to give her to them?'

Silence.

Saul shoved his chair away from the table but remained seated. 'Splinter, you haven't agreed have you? You can't.'

Splinter looked down at Saul. 'She is my sister. I shall do with her what I want.'

Saul was aghast. 'You are unbelievable.'

Splinter tried to smile back. 'I know I am. Now get out.'

'Your Majesty,' volunteered a voice from the depths of Splinter's head. 'Don't let him weaken you. You have to go through with this.'

'Do I?' Splinter found himself asking the voice.

'Of course you do,' it said.

'You do. Definitely,' said another.

'Well, maybe ...' began a third.

Splinter shut out the voices before there could be any more dissent.

'Get out,' he said to Saul. 'I don't need you. If you want

to make yourself useful, arrange for breakfast to be sent. I am hungry.'

When Saul remained sitting at the table, large fists clenched at his sides, Splinter leant down, nose to broken nose. 'Go.'

Without a further word, Saul left the room.

The audience chamber was a huge space and it was full but despite everything that was happening, Splinter noted that Saul was absent.

'Good,' he thought to himself. There was no room for doubters.

He sat on the twisted throne in the fifth alcove. Above him, the galleries were packed with so many different people. He recognised none of them but that didn't matter. All the faces dissolved into one blur of eyes focused on him. The vast floor of rose-coloured marble was lost beneath people who stretched before him, rank on rank. His attendants had explained that there were dukes and archdukes, princes and generals, presidents and chancellors, kings and queens. It was exactly like those scenes from the Omnicon to which he had devoted so many of his days and nights.

The costumes and uniforms were more diverse than he had expected but the Inquisitors had been diplomatic enough to ensure that only humans attended: at least, all the guests looked like humans. The purpose of the occasion was for everyone to pay attention to Splinter, not for him to sit gawping at a menagerie of freaks.

In the alcove next to Splinter sat Azgor. Malbane sat in the central alcove and after him sat Snargis and then Veer. Despite the finery of the grand assemblage, the Inquisitors wore their customary clothes and so did Splinter: the black, buttoned, high-collared jacket, the narrow black trousers, the long, black shoes. And his hair had been chopped so that now it was white and long and spiky, just as it had been before it had been dyed.

Splinter's eyes lingered on the fluted rostrum that stood like the base of a pillar, immediately before the thrones. On it there sat a crown. It was a simple, black circlet, narrow, with curved prongs like ravens' beaks. Beside the rostrum stood a figure in a white gown and a frowning mask: the sort of mask Splinter had seen on billboards outside the theatres where his fingers had been well occupied on busy nights. Malbane had told him that this person was called the coryphaeus and that he had been appointed specifically for the coronation.

Although they were difficult to see through the crowd, even from the raised seat of the throne, Splinter knew that at the far end of the chamber there were musicians. He caught the draw of a bow on strings, the dissonant blare of a trumpet, the bending roll of a drum being tuned.

Then there was silence. It fell so deep, so heavy that the hall felt as if it was sinking. Slowly, the music began: the pulse of weaving strings, the gentle woodwind as they spoke of struggles fought and battles won, and the righteous triumph as the trumpets and drums erupted and suddenly there was singing, people actually singing just like in the coronations he had watched and Splinter wanted to shout,

'Look at me! Look at what I have done! Look at what I am to become!'

He wanted to shout it loudly enough to shatter stone, to break bone, to draw tears from jewels; so loudly that his voice would fill the universes, from this audience chamber to the deepest sewer in the city.

Now, the coryphaeus was approaching with the crown held high, the grim mask warning Splinter of the heavy responsibilities he was assuming. But Splinter was ready. All his life he had been ready for this. He lowered his head and felt the iron rest upon it and when next he looked up, he knew that now, at last, he was a king.

He knew this music so well, and although these words sounded different from those he had listened to hundreds of times before, he knew the singing was drawing to its close. He looked at all the people and they looked back and they were happy.

They adore me, he realised.

And in the thrones beside him, Azgor, Malbane, Snargis and Veer were clapping and the ecstasy of what he had become seized him so overwhelmingly that he leapt from the throne of frozen flames and ran into the vaulted hall shouting over and over again, 'I am a king!'

He ran unevenly, his ankle a little sore, but he was rejoicing. The crowd backed away, bowing, but whether they stood and stared or retreated, he didn't care. Never in his life had he known happiness like this. He returned to his throne panting, welcomed by the indulgent smiles of his fellow Inquisitors.

His fellow Inquisitors!

The thought was so fine he nearly ran back into the chamber to continue his jubilation.

'Control yourself, Your Majesty,' said one voice.

'You are a king now,' said another.

They were right. With a proper display of decorum the King of Rats assumed his throne.

'Where has everybody gone?' he gasped when he saw the empty hall.

'The coronation is over, Splinter,' explained Malbane, patiently. 'And now you are a king.'

'But the coryphaeus has gone!' Splinter scanned all the empty space, the expanse of cold marble, the empty galleries, as if he might have missed one last guest.

'The musicians must have packed everything away so quickly,' he whispered in wonderment.

'You have your crown,' Malbane assured him.

'Yes. Yes,' murmured Splinter. 'But I don't feel all that different.'

'That is ... natural,' explained Malbane. 'Now you are one of us your power will grow, slowly at first, but it will grow.'

The coryphaeus had re-entered the hall by the lofty double doors at the far end and they closed behind him. He approached the thrones slowly and with an ornate chalice cupped in his hands.

'We have sat here for hours,' said Malbane. 'Now it is time for a little refreshment. Only a little, but sufficient to seal the bond between us.'

The chalice was presented to Veer, who sipped, and from Veer it was passed along the Inquisitors until it came to

Splinter. He looked over the brim and saw, to his relief, that it was still almost full of deep red liquor. He drank it in one long, hot draught and sat back with a fiery gasp.

'Better?' enquired Malbane, with a knowing smile.

'Much better,' sighed Splinter, the pleasure of kingship coursing through his blood. Inwardly, he scolded himself for being so silly. Now was no time to waver and, in truth, he did feel more powerful than before.

There were two loud blows against the far doors.

Malbane looked across at them as if his body had been electrified.

'Mevrad,' he hissed and along the line of Inquisitors the same name was repeated with gasps and snarls.

'Mevrad?' scorned Splinter. 'You mean Ethel?' He began to laugh. He could think of nothing finer than the old crone coming up against him and his fellow Inquisitors.

'What is she doing here?' Malbane's head was thrust forward, eyes fixed on the far doors like blowtorches.

'The bad fairy always turns up late,' suggested Splinter. 'She's probably brought a spinning wheel.'

The look that Malbane cast him was so venomous that Splinter squirmed back in his throne and shrugged.

'What?' He looked at the door, perplexed. 'It's only Ethel.'

CHAPTER 18

The far door flew open with a crash and into the audience chamber marched a tall woman with long, ebony hair. She wore the sort of gold and brown corseted gown that Splinter thought a mediaeval lady might wear, but her hair was loose and wild and her fiery, almond eyes were those of a tiger. She moved sinuously as the cats that padded either side of her.

One was large and grey with spotted fur, the other lean and tortoiseshell. Splinter recognised Argus and Sekhmet at once. When they were halfway across the chamber, Argus's body expanded into the stomping, bearded man with the eye-clustered cloak. With a head-splitting roar, Sekhmet stretched and grew, even as she walked, uncurling into a sand-pelted, barrel-chested, golden-eyed lioness. Sekhmet roared again, dark muzzle snarling, sabre teeth bared.

The coryphaeus turned from the thrones and emitted a squeal like air escaping from a balloon. He ran in a zig-zag from the Inquisitors and towards the far doors but before he could swerve past the visitors, Argus felled him with a blow from one of his brawny arms. There was a shriek and then the white gown collapsed to the floor, empty, as if the coryphaeus had been nothing more than a puppet. The frowning mask rolled away.

Splinter was astonished to see how the Inquisitors reared back in their thrones as the woman advanced towards them. Azgor hissed like a snake, Snargis's mouth vomited beetles and worms down his beggar's rags and Veer and Malbane both glowered as if their eyes could reduce flesh to flames. But the woman's boots strode across the marble floor and she seemed to grow in size as she approached so that by the time she stopped before the thrones, she loomed over them, flanked by the man and the lioness.

She pointed a long, bone-white finger at Malbane, the blood-red nail inches from his face.

'What have you done?' she demanded in a voice that boomed throughout the chamber.

Splinter remembered that voice from the first time he and Box and Chess met Ethel, when she had told them who she really was as they stood in the hunters' detention unit.

'You have no place here, Mevrad,' insisted Malbane, and Splinter was aghast at the tremor in his voice.

'You must go,' demanded Veer and as he did so, the hall darkened and his head expanded into a boiling mist that rushed out of the alcove like a geyser.

'Don't you dare to tell me what I must do,' roared the woman. Her black hair swirled like the night and her voice crashed against the thrones like the ocean and Veer reappeared, corporeal, with blood seeping from his nose. He groaned and slumped where he sat.

This is all wrong, Splinter cried out inside his head. His fellow Inquisitors should destroy this woman. Surely they could blot her out of existence by a twitch of their hands. It was only Ethel.

But it was obvious that it was not *only* Ethel. Splinter had always known that Ethel and the Baroness Mevrad Styx were the same person. However, after their first meeting she had always been Ethel: old, smelly, cantankerous, pathetic. He had forgotten about the voice. He had chosen to forget about her terrifying beauty.

But now he watched his fellow Inquisitors squirm where they sat and he wished he had remembered.

Only Malbane retained his composure. Anxiously, he said, 'You can do nothing here, Mevrad. It is not for you to intervene.'

'What have you done to him?' she demanded, with barely a glance at Splinter.

'I am a king,' said Splinter, but when Mevrad ignored him entirely he felt very stupid.

'What have you done, Malbane?' repeated Mevrad, and Sekhmet's throat rumbled. 'Pumping him so full of Dream he doesn't know reality from his own delusions?' She looked at Splinter then, but these were not Ethel's tired old eyes. These eyes scorched his soul. 'Have they been feeding you well, Splinter? Plenty to eat? Plenty to drink?'

'You cannot interfere with what we do,' ventured Malbane. 'You should not even speak.' He dared to lean out of his throne and ask, 'Do you want Bael here? Now? Shall we end it all, at once?' When Mevrad did not reply, Malbane said, 'I thought not.'

Then he was flung back in his seat and he groaned as

Mevrad pointed a finger at him, twisting it in the air as if she were driving it through his body.

'It would be very easy to end it now, Malbane. Very tempting. I could destroy all of you with no more effort than a curl of one finger.' She lowered her hand and Malbane collapsed forwards, gasping.

All along the thrones, the Inquisitors hissed and Splinter noticed how their bodies were shifting between hard flesh and vapour, as if they were slipping out of the human shapes they had assumed.

'But you are right,' conceded Mevrad. 'A direct clash between Bael and me would end everything and leave nothing. Nothing at all. Your destruction is not for me. But to use *him*,' she pointed at Splinter and he flinched even though he felt nothing, 'is not right.'

'We have never concerned ourselves with your obsession about what is *right*,' Malbane risked saying.

'No,' said Mevrad, icily. 'You want a world so ultimately controlled that it is nothing more than a paperweight for Bael to place on his desk. But,' and her eyes darkened and it seemed to Splinter that the whole chamber darkened with them, 'as long as I exist, and others like me, there will be freedom. There will be *choice*.'

Steeling himself, Malbane pointed at Splinter and said, 'This is *his* choice. There is nothing you can do to interfere. You must prepare yourself for defeat, Mevrad. You got to the girl first, it is true. But we shall have her at the end.'

Mevrad looked about as if she expected to see someone who wasn't there. Then she said to Splinter, 'I remember a boy called Splinter. He had intelligence and courage and a

-[268]-

mind of his own. But he complained, always, that he never had a free choice. I see that he has made his choice now.' She cast her tigerish eyes along the row of Inquisitors and each of them cowered as she did so.

'I hope you are satisfied with your choice, Splinter.' Then she smiled at him, but with pity or derision, he couldn't tell. 'I hope your imagination gave you a good coronation,' and with a hint of Ethel, she reached out, patting his wrinkled hand and then lifting her hand to the shrivelled skin of his face. 'I hope it was worth it, Splinter.'

Then the Baroness Mevrad Styx turned on the heel of her boot and strode away from the Inquisitors, ebony hair trailing, body lithe as the lioness that padded beside her.

At the doors she stopped and without turning round she said, 'It's never too late to make the right choice. Never.'

Then she and Argus and Sekhmet left and the silence was too loud to bear.

'What is Dream?' asked Splinter, hesitant.

'Dreams,' muttered Malbane. 'She meant have we been filling your head full of dreams?'

That, at least, made sense to Splinter. Had they been filling his head full of dreams? No, he decided. These were his dreams, not theirs. The Inquisitors had simply made them come true. He was more unsettled by how they had let Mevrad treat them as she had, as if they had no choice. As if they were weak.

I could destroy all of you with no more effort than a curl of one finger.

He wished he had thought more about that first meeting with Ethel, in the detention unit. But it wasn't his fault if she chose to go around acting like a pathetic old bag lady. How was he to know? She should have told him.

'She *did* tell you, Your Majesty,' a voice reminded him. 'She told you the first time she met you.'

'I wish I had remembered, his own voice said quietly.

'Now,' said Malbane. 'You and I need to talk, Splinter.'

'I'm quite tired.' Suddenly he didn't feel like talking with Malbane.

'Then I shall ensure you have some refreshment, but talk we must.' Malbane was adamant.

'Just you and Splinter?' asked Veer, wiping blood from his face with a white handkerchief.

'I think that would be best, as we discussed.'

Veer dissolved into vapour which vanished. When Splinter next looked, the thrones that had held Snargis and Azgor were also empty.

'How do they do that?' he marvelled.

'A thousand lifetimes of scientific knowledge, a profound appreciation of the deepest laws of physics, and fierce concentration.' Malbane stepped down from his throne, straightened his cowl and beckoned to Splinter. 'We have to talk now.'

Splinter slipped off his throne. He felt the manacle weight of the bargain he had made with the Twisted Symmetry. Now that he had been crowned, he had space to consider what he was doing. He should have been elated but, as usual, Ethel had spoilt everything. However, this time he didn't think she had been stupid or pathetic. She had spoilt things because she had the power to spoil them.

'I'm not sure how I can make so much difference to whether you can catch Chess,' he began.

'Oh, Splinter,' croaked Malbane, putting an arm round his shoulders, 'you will make *all* the difference.' His venerable face smiled. 'She trusts you.'

Pictures flashed through Splinter's mind like a film. The day he took Chess and Box away from the Elms Orphanage, the time he had taken her climbing to the highest roofs at the wharf, showing her the best places to put her feet and she listening to his instructions as if they were law. He remembered the chaos the day that the hunters had raided the wharf and how Chess and Box followed him away from the ledge, and he remembered how he and Chess had sat in a rowing boat off the coast on Surapoor and she had asked him to help her.

'She always wanted my help,' Splinter said, quietly, and he swallowed back the memories.

'That is why you can help us now,' coaxed Malbane. He escorted Splinter across the marble floor, the two of them miniature beneath the arching beams of the audience chamber.

'She was very bossy,' continued Splinter as they walked. 'But that's what happens when people get older, I suppose. But even when she was like that, she still wanted my help. She asked for it.'

'Of course she did.' Malbane's voice was reassuring. They had entered a cloister. The sky above the adjacent quadrangle was immense and blue but within the cloister it was comfortingly murky. 'She knew how important you were.

She probably told you, time and again, how important you were. How special.'

'Well, no,' admitted Splinter, face hardening. 'She didn't go that far.'

'Ah, I see.' Malbane smiled.

'But maybe . . .' began Splinter.

Malbane took his arm. 'Listen to me, Splinter. The truth can be painful, but we have to face it. Did Chess ever tell you how special you are?'

'Not in so many words,' replied Splinter. But she wanted me to help, he thought. She trusted me.

'Did she ever ask you what *you* wanted?'

'No. But once she said that she wanted a leather jacket and a pair of trainers.'

'It sounds, if you don't mind me saying so, as if your little sister spent a lot of time thinking about herself.'

'All the time.' Splinter wanted to convince himself of that, as much as to tell the Inquisitor.

Malbane pushed open a little wooden door. Inside there was a low-ceilinged study with two armchairs, a fireplace, before the fireplace a table with a decanter, two sparkling glasses and a plate of biscuits, and in the far wall, a mullioned, lead-latticed window.

'Come in, Splinter,' he said. 'We must have our little chat.'

The fire was burning. It crackled gently but was not too hot.

'Sit down.' Malbane handed Splinter a glass filled with white wine and he poured one for himself. 'Please, take some biscuits.'

Splinter bit into a biscuit with a loud snap. It was tasteless but the wine was better. He drank down the glass and Malbane recharged it. He noticed that on the table, next to the decanter, there was a long wooden box.

'Power isn't easy, Splinter.'

Splinter nodded. He was beginning to understand that.

'There is always more than one way of looking at a situation,' continued the Inquisitor, kicking off his sandals and wiggling his toes before the flames. 'So the only thing is to do what matters: to you.'

'What matters to *you*?' asked Splinter.

Malbane reflected upon this at length before saying in a hoarse voice, 'Not dying.'

Splinter sniffed. 'We could all say that.'

'I am a human, like you,' said Malbane. 'Or I was. So was Behrens, who I am sorry to say you never met. Azgor, Veer, Snargis are not human, although they have been doing their best for you. Snargis encounters a little difficulty in distinguishing between species, and enjoys the undulating sensation of crawlers, hence his pestilential infestations.'

Malbane sipped his wine thoughtfully. 'I am older than many of the stars now, but I haven't forgotten my life: my real life, that short life I was given like every other human. Just long enough to learn the fear of losing everything. Have you ever been in love, Splinter?'

Splinter felt himself blush. Whatever else he had expected from the Inquisitors, it wasn't a conversation like this.

Malbane shook his head. 'Love never ends so long as we have memories. And memories never end so long as we *live*.' The Inquisitor's vehemence made Splinter edgy. He shifted in his chair.

'My cleverness with time saved only me, Splinter, but I have memories. As long as I am alive, so is she.' He turned his wise old eyes on Splinter. 'I don't want to die because I want to keep her alive.' He chuckled to himself as if he found himself a bit foolish. 'I don't want to die because of love. What makes you want to live forever, Splinter?'

Splinter looked into the fire gloomily. All he had wanted was to become an Inquisitor, to become a king and now here he was, with the crown to prove it. He removed the crown, turned it in his hands and hooped it over one of the arms of the chair.

'I don't know,' he sighed.

'Of course you do,' Malbane encouraged him, standing up and ruffling Splinter's white hair, suddenly all avuncular. 'You're a purist, Splinter. You want this for the sake of itself: purely for power. Power for power's sake: motives come no purer than that.'

He picked up the wooden box but didn't open it yet. 'And to keep power, you must be decisive. You know that.'

Splinter nodded. He did know that. That was how he had come this far. 'Ruthless brilliance,' he muttered.

'Exactly, yes, ruthless brilliance.' Malbane tapped the corner of the box on the table like a conductor's baton. 'Ruthless brilliance; I like that.'

He paced to the window, the light catching the folds of his hood, the box held behind his back. 'Now, about your sister. She has become very powerful herself.'

He appeared to ruminate upon this further before saying, 'She has become a threat to all of us.'

'If she is so powerful, how do we catch her?' Splinter rubbed his face.

'We force her to make a choice.'

'A choice?' Splinter had grown suspicious of the language of choice.

'A choice to be with you.' Malbane advanced from the window, his grey head inches beneath the low ceiling. 'We know that she trusts you.'

'Anna told me.' Even in here, deep amongst the Twisted Symmetry, it felt good to think of Anna, just to use her name.

'Anna?' Malbane cocked an eyebrow before continuing. 'Chess is learning the science of the dimensions.'

Splinter laughed and shook his head.

'Believe me, Splinter, her power is impressive.'

That comment found its way into Splinter like a gimlet. He wasn't here to listen to Malbane pay compliments to his selfish little sister. Splinter noticed now his dark scowl met with an approving nod from the Inquisitor.

'Good,' said Malbane. 'I was beginning to wonder whether you had forgotten all that we have done for you.'

'Can't you just send your armies after her?'

'Too messy, too unpredictable and too much *noise*. Even at a time like this, we must exercise some discretion in our operations; too much attention is never helpful. But,' an Inquisitorial finger was wagged, 'how to gain the initiative?'

'Surprise her?' volunteered Splinter.

'I understand you were present when General Vane finally took the Traitor captive?'

'I organised it,' trumpeted Splinter.

'Then, I see that you have a talent for these things. Well, you will recall that even a pan-dimensional creature cannot escape the grip of the xenrian gaolers; they penetrate every fraction of space to a sub-atomic degree. Once Chess has been locked down she will be utterly helpless. All you have to do, Splinter, is to lure her within range of the gaolers.'

'But how will you make her come to me?'

'Dogs, Splinter, dogs. Your sister has had a bad experience with dogs, hasn't she?'

'We all have,' commented Splinter. Nothing canine could be trusted.

'You have heard of neural sculpting?' When Splinter hesitated, Malbane added, 'You are familiar with the construction of metalbacks are you not?'

Shrieks. Wings. Beaks. Screams. The tearing of flesh. Splinter blanched.

'I see that you are,' smiled Malbane. 'The same technology has been employed by the warps utilising nervous tissue from hunting dogs. Combined with amarantium at a molecular level they have engineered highly effective hunters; no longer dogs at all in fact but machines; hunting machines with teeth.'

Splinter wasn't sure he liked the sound of that. 'They can pass through different worlds because of the amarantium?'

'Exactly.' Malbane sat on a chair arm. 'We have used them with great success, in your world as well.' He laughed quietly and shook his head. 'Myths and legends about ghostly hunts coursing the moors and forests in the dead of night? Long may humans be masters of the subtle art of self-deception.'

'So what about Chess?' asked Splinter, biting a fingernail

as he contemplated hunting machines with teeth.

Malbane looked into the fire. 'We know where your sister is and we know how closely the Blood Sentinels have been watching over her. But she has been very foolish. She has distanced herself from her friends and protectors. Now she is as vulnerable as she has ever been. We have three stygian packs ready, primed with her blood. She has been so careless, leaving it wherever she goes.'

'They follow blood like spooks?'

'Similar. But whereas a spook is used to track, stygian packs are used to track and kill.'

'But you don't want her dead!'

'We want her terrified,' explained Malbane. 'And that is when you will offer her a way out.'

'A way straight to you?'

'Precisely. If she is frightened enough there will be no hesitation. She will come.'

'And afterwards?' asked Splinter. 'What will happen to Chess after she is with you?'

'With *us*, Splinter, with *us*,' Malbane corrected him. 'We shall explain to her the merits of our point of view and she will help us. Nothing nasty. I am confident that once we have completed our ... explanation, Chess will be *begging* to help us.'

Splinter rubbed his face with both hands. 'And I have to do this?'

'Splinter, you are one of us now.' Malbane smiled. 'I think you still do not believe me.' He tapped the box. 'That is why I am going to give you a present. Something from me to you.'

Slowly, he lifted the lid from the box. Inside there was a

knife: stiletto-thin with a pale blue handle and a plain, semi-circular hand guard.

'A crystal knife,' whispered Malbane. 'What's wrong?' he asked as Splinter drew back.

'Surprise, that's all.' Splinter wasn't going to say anything about what the Codex had shown him: a knife just like this in the hand of a faceless man. A knife that would kill him were it given the chance.

But this knife was a gift. He leant forwards.

'On no account touch the blade. It is forged from pure amarantium. But keep the knife.' The box was passed between them. 'Nothing can escape that blade, Splinter.' Malbane stared into his eyes. 'See how I value you? How I trust you?'

Splinter nodded.

'Good. As I said, you are one of us now.' The Inquisitor stood. 'So let us deal with your sister. There is no more time to . . . spend in conversation.'

'Chess? Already?' asked Splinter, tearing his eyes from the crystal knife.

'Of course, Splinter. *Now*. What else are you here for?'

CHAPTER 19

Box yawned, cracked his knuckles and stretched his neck. Today was going to be different.

There had been no morning training. The aerial walkways and machine-gun nests were packed with guards, far more than usual, doubtless gathered to enjoy the coming spectacle. But they had fallen silent, idly watching the Fleshings below, or checking the firing mechanisms of their weapons in a succession of clicks, snaps and shots of gun oil. By late morning, Six, the Yard Master, had still not been seen.

The Fleshings were as subdued as the guards who watched over them. They sat about the huge arena in small groups, picking at the sand, murmuring half-heartedly, dozing listlessly. They wore the rags that their clothes had been reduced to over these past months. Where they had fur, it was matted by dust and dried blood. Their faces were hard, expressionless. They knew that today there would be no sword drill, no hours at the machines and no nightfall. Today was going to be different. Today, they were going to die.

From the way that the sun had not yet climbed to its highest point, and from the way that the strip of shadow along the foot of the wall was still cool, Box knew that it was late morning. He leant back, enjoying the coldness of the smooth stone and let his mind flow back to yellow mornings at the wharf, when he and the other rats would bask in the sun before heading into the city for the day's graft.

Sunlight brought its own peace. Jacks went on holidays where they bought more sunlight, but Box was content with the sun he got for free: early mornings flicking stones into the river, ragging his friends or just sinking into nothingness for an hour or so. Grease couldn't buy you that.

'What are you so pleased about?' drawled Razool, from the side of his mouth, dark dog-eyes heavy-lidded and half-shut as he sat, legs outstretched, beside Box.

'Going home,' Box muttered back. He no longer had to work out which words to use. He had lived amongst the snouts for so long, eating, training, fighting, that their rough dialect of Chat and slang came to him naturally.

'Home?' Razool snorted, and shook his black-maned, Alsatian-sharp face. 'There's a lot of universe to see, Box. Home is for whelps.'

Box opened an eye to look sidelong at the lean, dark-skinned snout. 'You never told me why they branded you a mutineer.'

Razool traced the bright pink scars on his left arm and chest. They were as clear and intricate as tattoos. 'It's a long story. If we get through today, maybe I'll tell it to you.'

'Get through today? We've not even had any slavver.' Box shut his eyes again.

'You know why you're not frightened, Box?'

'No,' grunted Box.

'Because you're too busy thinking about your belly.'

Box patted the hard-muscled contours of his stomach. 'Priorities,' he murmured. 'It's all about priorities.'

But Box's priority was not his stomach. His priority was getting out of here and getting back to Chess. Today, he would spill any amount of blood to do that.

Ten minutes passed, during which the sun turned on them and the heat beat down.

'You know what to do when we start?' muttered Box, eyes shut. 'You've told the others?'

'Yup,' Razool muttered back, eyes shut too, voice sleepy as a buzzing fly. 'Now stop yapping and let me get some zip.' He began to snore, quietly. Box began to doze too, lulled by the muted, nervous chat of the other Fleshings.

'Get up.' The hoarse, sibilant voice of Six stirred him from sleep. Box blinked hot sunlight out of his eyes and rolled onto his side before standing. He slapped the sand off his leggings and swallowed stale spit.

Six stood in the centre of the arena, emaciated thorax swaying side to side on its tubular spine, cobra-like, as he observed the rabble.

'Today,' he announced, 'you will fulfil your purpose. You will fight hard and die well. And you *will* die. Today, there is an extra cadre of cadets: five hundred against a couple of hundred of you. With so many of them, they will be hungry for a kill.'

The bloody glow of the scrutator swung left, then right. 'I am sure you will not disappoint them.'

'Five hundred?' Raxa growled under his breath. 'Five hundred? That's too many.'

'We don't have a hope,' agreed Skarl.

A murmur crept through the snouts: there was no chance, this was impossible, it would be a blood-bath. Eyes turned to Box to see how he reacted to what Six had told them, to see whether they would be standing by the plan.

Box spat into the dirt. Quietly, he said to Razool, 'A lot of cadets will die today.'

From the barred gate through which the machines were hauled came a detachment of guards wheeling the weapon coffers. Four guards pushed the long trolleys and eight more marched alongside, blaze carbines shouldered. They withdrew beyond arm's reach, weapons trained on the Fleshings as they took their mace-blades.

'The cadets will enter by the main arch and form in ranks before advancing.' Six jabbed his narrow chin towards the doorway through which the Fleshings had first entered the Yard, currently sealed by a screen of stone. 'You may adopt whatever formation you wish.' He chuckled with a tubercular wheeze. 'It will make no difference, but we are kind enough to let you choose how you wish to be slaughtered.'

Box took two mace-blades: one for each hand. He released both blades, checking the action, slicing the air, easing his shoulders with a pattern of lunges and blocks. Sweat ran from his broad chest, but his palms were dry.

'I shall watch you with particular interest, boy.'

Box stopped, realising that Six was addressing him.

'As I have said, you remind me of how I once was.'

—[282]—

Box snorted and spat into the dirt.

Six's laughter hissed like a cold breeze. '*Exactly* as I once was.'

The wheels of the trolleys squealed over the dust as the guards hurriedly pushed them away. But Six remained amongst the Fleshings.

'The slaughter will begin in five minutes,' he announced. 'I shall be watching. Do not let me down. Die well.' His carcass-like ribcage twitched with laughter as his long, bowed legs took him stalking to the far end of the Yard.

The Fleshings stood in knots, straggled about the arena, mace-blades ready. There was a deepening silence. The heat intensified, humming through the slatted roof. The only movement was the sweat which trickled down hairless skin. All eyes were on the entrance screen.

When the screen slid back, the Fleshings automatically drew together, as if they would be safer that way. Many gathered about Box, instinct drawing them close to their best fighter.

Through the entrance came the Dog Troopers, so many and so quickly that it looked as if they were being poured into the Fleshing Yard. But they didn't look as Box had imagined. They wore the black uniforms to which he was accustomed, but not the slabs of body armour. Instead, each trooper was encased in a blur, as if their bodies were heating the air about them until it shimmered.

'Radiolarian force fields,' whispered Razool.

'Meaning?' Box wiped his brow with the back of his forearm.

'Meaning this is why Six is so confident none of us will

survive.' He shook back his mane and chuckled sardonically. 'Meaning this is going to be more difficult than expected.'

Box's fists tightened about the mace-blades. 'But not impossible.' His eyes narrowed as he sized up the troopers.

'I'll tell you that,' observed Razool, 'afterwards.' Then Razool raised his voice. 'Listen to me.' He spoke clearly, his voice loud enough for the Fleshings to hear. Opposite them, the troopers were forming into rows, boots kicking up clouds of dust. 'Blades are useless against the armour they're wearing. But there are three weak points: the neck, the wrist and the knee. Strike there and only there.'

There was a stirring amongst the snouts; they were hungry for a voice that could command them.

'You know what to do,' continued Razool. 'Fight up the right wall and hold the ground in front of the gate.'

All eyes flicked to the bars through which the weapon coffers had just been wheeled, now hard to the ground. Then all eyes turned back to Razool.

'You ready for the gate?' Razool muttered to Box; the gate through which the training machines were brought; the gate through which the weapons had been wheeled; the gate through which guards came and went. A gate that must lead into the complex.

'Can't wait,' Box muttered back.

At the other end of the Yard an order was given. It echoed to the far wall and back and five hundred mace-blades were released with a scything hiss. Now the deep wave of troopers glinted with silver teeth.

Razool circled, looking at the hoard of snouts who surrounded him. 'Hold the gate. Understand?' Rough, scarred heads nodded. There were loud snorts, low growls, the hefting of blades, the baring of fangs. The ground drummed as the troopers began to advance in ranks spanning the width of the Yard, churning the dust.

'Are you ready?' shouted Razool. He was answered by grunts.

Box felt his heart pumping hard, adrenalin coursing through his veins. This was no time for doubt, for blades held weakly, for anything other than fighting until the fighting ended in death or victory. It was very simple.

'Are you ready?' he yelled.

This time there was a raw cry of, 'Yes.'

He shook both blades by his sides and yelled again, 'Are you ready?' and the snouts howled back their answer.

He faced the wall of troopers that was rolling towards them. 'Then fight!' he roared, and as he charged so did the rest of the Fleshings, howling, roaring, snarling.

They sped up the right side of the Yard so that their full force was taken by only a small section of the troopers. This was not what the troopers had expected and at first their ranks were broken and smashed back by the concentrated force of the Fleshings. But the cadets were quick to react and the centre and far ranks swung round in an arc so that the Fleshings were caught in a crescent. But to their backs there was the gate. Now they had to hold the battling ranks of the Dog Troopers for as long as it took.

But the troopers would not be held back for long; there were so many of them and they were safe from any but the most accurate blows. Already a crimson pool of blood leaked across the sand from the Fleshings who had been hacked down, their pelts and rough skin defenceless against the storm of mace-blades. The cadets surged forwards, each vying for a kill, desperate to experience the striking down of life when there were so few targets.

Box and Razool were close to the gate as the first of the cadets broke through the Fleshings; three of them, weapons smeared with blood, haughty in their impregnable body armour, hungry to meet with the boy and the lean, black-maned mutineer who came running at them. If Box wanted to get to the gate, he had to get past these snouts. The slaughter to his left was so furious that more troopers would break through in seconds.

Razool ran in and his blade clanged against the first cadet's. But before his opponent could strike again, Razool had dropped to one knee and hamstrung the cadet with a slash to the back of the knee. Box didn't see what happened next because he faced two troopers blocking the way.

Fight clever: Box had never forgotten what Balthazar had taught him.

Not checking his sprint, he sprang up off his left foot and as his right made contact with the trooper's chest, he pushed up as if still sprinting and kicked his left leg forwards, driving his heel into the trooper's face.

The trooper began to fall and Box spun off his chest, shearing both his mace-blades across the next trooper's neck as he turned through the air. The blades closed, slicing through fur, skin, muscle, arteries, windpipe, vertebrae; and the headless body dropped to the floor.

Now, Box stood before the barred gate. Now was the time to carry through what he and Razool had planned.

Two guards stood there, enjoying the spectacle. Always, there were two guards here. Before their jaws could drop, before their gloved hands could pull up their carbines, Box had hurled both blades through the bars. The guards had been standing close. The steel blades thudded handle-deep into their chests.

All those years, playing with knives . . .

They hadn't hit the ground before Razool had thrown his bloodied mace-blade to Box. Box grabbed it from the air, retracted the blade and flung the long, heavy mace grip at the control pad set five metres into the tunnel.

All those years throwing stones at windows, at cars, at the crashers, at each other . . .

The mace thumped hard into the pad and the gate began to rise.

As soon as there was space, Razool rolled under the rising bars, followed closely by Box. Whilst Box punched the control panel to stop the gate rising any further, Razool freed the blaze carbines from the dead guards, cocking both as he knelt by the bodies. Box saw how expertly he handled the weapons.

'Ever used one of these?' asked Razool.

'Nope,' said Box.

'OK. The rounds come out of that end,' Razool pointed to one of the muzzles, 'and you pull the trigger at the other. Just make sure you hold it the right way round. Think you can manage that?'

'Sounds tricky,' said Box, 'but if something as stupid as a snout can do it, I should be OK.'

Razool threw him a carbine. Box caught it with both

hands. It was lighter than he had expected. He tucked the stock under his arm, right hand wrapped round the grip. The gateway was packed with Fleshings, which meant that he and Razool were hidden from the view of the roof guards. With the gate open by only a metre or so, they wouldn't know what was happening. That was good. Surprise was everything.

'Skarl. Raxa,' shouted Box. The two snouts looked back from the other side of the bars. 'Hold them off until the firing starts, then fall back in here.'

Skarl nodded, wolf face spattered with blood. Raxa snarled in acknowledgement, mace-blade dripping gore. The fighting was not all one way.

'No firing until we're up there,' Razool warned Box.

But the longer this took, the more of their comrades would die. 'Let's go,' urged Box, running towards the ramp at the end of the tunnel. Now they were entering unknown territory.

The ramps were long and gently sloping, turning back on themselves as they climbed to the roof. Although other passageways led onto them, there were no guards. The thrill of watching the slaughter had drawn them out to the overhead walkways. Box and Razool didn't stop sprinting. The months of merciless training had left them hard-muscled and fit. Side by side, they took the ramps, carbines at their hips.

Near the top, they ran into two guards. The guards came round the final corner, literally walking into Box and Razool. Box was the first to react. Flipping round his blaze carbine, he caught the barrel with both hands and swung the stock into the side of the first guard's head, then drove the other guard into the wall with a side-kick. Before the trooper had swung up the nose of his carbine, Razool had snatched the mace-blade from the guard's belt and released it into his shaggy throat.

'I thought dogs were meant to be loyal,' said Box, as the body slumped to the floor.

'They are,' replied Razool, 'but not always to other dogs. Come on.'

They edged up to the end of the passage. It was full of daylight and the sounds of the fighting from the arena below. When Box inched an eye around the corner, he saw about a dozen guards crammed along the high gantry and at the far end, the long-barrelled machine gun sitting in its circular nest. There were another five machine-gun nests, all interconnected by the walkways that criss-crossed beneath the roof. Up here, the sunlight was white, cutting into the gloom in bright strips from the desert sky above, glinting off the silver symbol that the guards wore on the shoulders of their black tunics; the awlis, the sign of the Twisted Symmetry.

Box and Razool leant back against the wall, carbines hugged to their sweating chests. They had to time this properly, but time wasn't something they had much of if the bloodbath in the Fleshing Yard wasn't going to turn into a slaughter.

'Safety-catch off,' whispered Razool, flicking the catch with his thumb. Box copied. 'Change lever to burst fire.' Razool turned the dial in the housing by the barrel.

'Up to five hundred rounds in one minute,' recited Box,

recalling what Balthazar had told him, many months before.

'Very good, Box.' Razool raised his brows, impressed by this piece of knowledge. 'But try not to fire them all at once. Fire in bursts. Short bursts.'

'Sure.'

'I go first. Then you cover me whilst I get to the gun. Got it?'

'Yup.'

Razool's dark eyes, more dog than man, looked intently at Box. 'I'd never have thought it; fighting alongside a skin.' He shook his mane.

'Watch closely,' said Box. 'You might learn a thing or two.'

'Ready?'

Box nodded. 'Ready.'

Razool spun off the wall, carbine at his shoulder. The rounds screamed down the walkway, bullet casings streaming from the breach. Then he was pounding over the sprawled bodies and it was Box's turn to step out from the passage, carbine ready.

This was a different world from the dirt floor of the Fleshing Yard. There was height and light and his eyes were level with the guards who were only just reacting to what was happening.

Box squeezed the trigger. The blaze carbine came alive in his hands, roaring out bullets and climbing up and left. He staggered back, unbalanced by the recoil.

'Take it steady,' yelled Razool, swinging into the bucket seat behind the machine gun, pulling down the barrels which were nose up. 'But keep firing.'

Along the nearest gantry, the guards were hoisting their

rifles over the handrail. Box braced himself, clenched his jaw and combed the walkway with a blaze of fire. He saw the black uniforms jolt backwards, limbs jerking.

He snatched a second carbine from one of the bodies at his feet and with both weapons braced in his sturdy arms, he spun round, raking the adjacent walkway with a blistering fire. Sparks danced off the handrails before the rounds levelled and thumped into the guards, who had only moments to return fire.

Box emptied the magazines in alternate bursts. When he had finished, nothing moved on the platform. Blue smoke trailed from the glowing muzzles of the blaze carbines.

Now the heavy machine gun roared into life. The long barrels whirred and flung out a crushing weight of lead that tore girders, smashed the other guns out of the roof and cut down guards like corn. Razool worked the gears skilfully, spinning the gun to face the different targets before they could return fire.

Incoming rounds rattled across the girders. Box threw down his carbines and snatched two fresh ones from the bodies at his feet. He dashed along the walkway towards Razool, ready to cover the snout. Bullets sang at his heels but he gritted his teeth and kept running. Razool had already swung the machine gun round and now it was blasting a wave of lead over Box's head, silencing the incoming fire. But in turning to cover Box, Razool had exposed his own back to a cluster of troopers who were bedded in behind the smouldering frame of a machine gun on the other side of the Fleshing Yard roof. Now they opened up, flames ripping from the carbine muzzles.

Box fired from his hip as he ran, making no effort to shield himself. It was vital to make the guards take cover; if they hit Razool, neither of them would stand a chance. His ears were numb from the blast of the automatic fire, and the heat of the gun barrels scorched his forearms, but the guards pulled back, waiting for an opportunity to return fire. They wouldn't have to wait long because there was no way Box cold keep up this rate of fire for more than seconds.

But before the magazines were spent, Razool had spun the big gun round. It pumped out rounds so fast that the machine gun opposite was smashed out of its housing, crashing down into the arena in an explosion of dirt. By the time that Razool released the trigger, there were no guards left to harry them.

Box stood back to back with Razool. He surveyed the wreckage of the walkways, a fresh carbine in his hands. His eyes were sharp for movement but there was none.

'All clear,' he said, not ceasing to look for the sly adjustment of a limb, the levelling of a gun barrel in their direction. 'Time to finish this, Zool.'

Razool angled the machine gun down, to the place where the trooper cadets and the Fleshings were still locked in hand-to-hand combat. All that remained of the Fleshings was a small, blood-spattered knot, in front of the gate.

'Let's even the odds.' Razool bared his fangs and pulled the trigger. The spray of bullets smashed open the ranks of the troopers, which spilt bodies to the floor like wood chippings.

Box looked over Razool's shoulder as a tall, serpentine body loped out of the margin and into the centre of the Yard.

He saw Razool bring the cross-hairs of the machine gun sights onto the Yard Master.

'No.' Box grasped the dark pelt of Razool's forearms. 'Don't kill the way out of this place.'

Razool uttered a low growl but stopped firing immediately.

Six raised his skeletal, metal-bonded dog head towards them, narrow, elongated, spine bowing backwards. 'Very wise,' he hissed.

The cadets still outnumbered the Fleshings by many hundreds, but they had fallen back when the machine-gun had cut into them. They made no effort to close with their opponents now. In front of the gate were clustered no more than twenty gore-streaked Fleshings, mace-blades clutched in their fists, their fallen comrades heaped at their feet. Amongst the dead were the black-uniformed bodies of troopers.

A hollow slapping noise came from Six as he clapped his withered right arm against his drum-skinned pelvis. 'Very good. Very good.' The scrutator focused on Box. 'Just like me,' and he chuckled hoarsely.

'We've won our passage out of here, Six,' shouted Box. His voice echoed across the smoking stillness of the arena.

'You certainly have, boy.'

'And Razool.'

'With pleasure.'

Raxa and Skarl and a handful more Fleshings had joined the rest from where they had been holding back troopers just inside the gate.

'And the others.' Box shook the carbine as he yelled in the harsh dog-tongue, now as natural to him as his own. 'All of us have won our way out of here.' His voice was raw: defiant but drained.

'All of you have won,' began Six, 'nothing. And I shall give it to you.' He spun out his pincer-tipped left arm. It extended ten metres, wrenching the corpse of a Fleshing out of the lifeless heap. He gripped the fur-patched, man-skinned body by its flaccid neck, feet dangling off the floor, head lolling like a puppet's.

'Better to be him than you,' croaked Six. 'Far better where he has gone than where you will be going.'

Six dropped the body to the dust and walked directly beneath the machine-gun nest where Box stood by Razool. The cadets rippled away from him as he did so.

'You will be sent to the penal battalions, boy: you, the mutineer and this mangy scum who failed to die today.' He arched his head round to cast his good eye over the Fleshings and he curled his lips into a smile. 'The death you cheated here will hunt you down in the Final Starfields. Unless you are very, *very* lucky,' and he swung his head up to eyeball Box.

'You know what?' drawled Razool, sliding out of the gun seat and clapping a hand on Box's shoulder.

'What?' muttered Box. A cut to the back of his right hand began to throb.

'I think you *are* lucky.' Razool turned his back on Six's scarlet glare and steered Box towards the tunnel that would take them back to where the other Fleshings were waiting for them.

'You know what?' said Box, dropping the carbine and feeling half a smile break at the edge of his mouth.

'What?'

'I think I am.'

He'd been told there was no escape from the prison on this planet and he'd escaped. He'd been told that there was no surviving the Fleshing Yards and, together with his blood-streaked comrades, he'd survived. He might not have been as smart as Splinter but he could fight and that was what mattered. He'd fought his way out of here and he would fight his way back to Chess, wherever she was. All he needed were his friends, his fists and a little more luck.

CHAPTER 20

The heavy roll of traffic on the flyovers deadened as Pacer and Gemma climbed the stairs to 11A Knott Street. They left damp footprints on the bare treads and the hiss of the rain through the open door muffled the sound of their steps. But here, in the Undergrove, a three-block grid of derelict, brick tenements, there would be no one to hear them; apart from the person they were looking for.

The gloom was deepened by the evening rain, rain that fell in straight lines from a lead sky, everything motionless apart from the relentless downpour. Only the dust stirred, rising and falling in the half-light of the stairwell.

They found her huddled on the floor by the fireplace, chin on her knees as she stared at the dilapidated armchair opposite. Apart from the armchair there was nothing in the room. She held a chess piece in her hand, a knight.

'How did you find me?' Chess didn't look at the boy and girl standing in the doorway. Her eyes fixed themselves on the horse's head as if it were fascinating.

'We know you, Chess,' said Pacer. 'That's how.'

'Everyone's been looking everywhere.' Gemma's fingers

alighted on a drooping tongue of wallpaper. Idly she pulled it, tearing more free and dislodging little chunks of mouldy plaster. 'You told us that you found your mum here so Pacer and me guessed that if you weren't anywhere else, you'd probably be here.' She grinned at Chess. 'And we were right.' Then she opened her other hand, revealing the crumpled leaf she'd been holding. 'See? I always find a green leaf when I'm going to find you.' Her bare feet left dark prints on the floorboards as she entered the room.

'It's been weeks, Chess.' Pacer walked across to the windows and leant against one of the metal screens that had been fastened over them. 'You can't just vanish. Well, *you* can vanish, but you always come back. And you can't spend your whole life looking at an armchair.'

'Where's Anna?' asked Chess, uncertainly.

'Hockey. It's a Thursday.' Pacer pressed his face against the screen. Little points of light dotted his dark skin and black combats. 'She didn't mean anything, Chess. She was only trying to look out for you.'

Chess exhaled slowly, stretched out her legs and put the chess piece in her pocket. 'Well, it got me thinking. I need to be on my own.' She scraped thick chestnut hair away from her face. 'And I haven't spent the whole time staring at that armchair. I've been practising.'

'Practising what?' Pacer sounded incredulous.

Chess shrugged and wrinkled her nose as if she wasn't sure what to make of her activities herself. 'My stuff. I think I'm ready.'

'Ready? What for?' Pacer looked about as if checking that

he hadn't missed something that was happening elsewhere in the room. Then he looked back at her.

Chess's brown eyes were fixed on his. 'For facing the enemy, if it comes to it.' Her voice was less steady than her gaze.

'Chess, you can't do that on your own.' Pacer held up a hand. 'I mean, if anyone could, it would be you, OK? But you can't. You mustn't.'

'Why've you come?'

'We're your friends, Chess,' said Gemma, as if it was so obvious it didn't need saying.

'I've never left you, Chess,' began Pacer, before stumbling over his words. 'I mean, *we've* never left you. Have we? We don't want you to be on your own now.'

'I like being on my own,' said Chess, not very convincingly.

'Well, maybe we like being with *you*.' Pacer pushed himself away from the screen. 'Maybe we want to be with you, Chess. Maybe we should have said that, OK? But we've always been together, so we shouldn't hardly need to say that.' He groped about for words. 'We're used to you being there and we want you there. So you don't need to be here, like this.'

Chess held Pacer's eyes in her gaze as if they were listening to one another without saying anything. Then she shook her head and got up, smacking dust off her jeans and jacket.

'Anna went after Ravillious on her own because that was best for everybody else. Well, it's like that with me. I'm sorry, Pacer.'

'You're still mad with Anna,' he accused her.

'No, not mad. Not any more.' Chess shrugged. 'I just see

things differently. Sometimes, after you've been really hurt, you see things . . . *better*. Don't you?'

Pacer opened his mouth to say something, then clenched his jaw shut.

Chess rubbed the side of Pacer's forearm. 'I don't think I'm part of you all any more. I hate it but I'm stuck with it.' Her voice was very soft. 'You don't have to be here.'

'I *want* to be here,' said Pacer, hoarsely.

Chess lowered her arm. She walked towards the door. 'Please, don't come looking for me again.'

'You can't stop us.' Gemma stepped aside.

'I think it's going to be very difficult for you to find me,' said Chess with a wan smile.

'Difficult doesn't matter to friends,' stated Gemma.

They heard Chess walk quickly down the stairs. Gemma pressed her nose up to the screen. 'She's going down the street,' she said. 'Shall we follow her?'

'No,' sighed Pacer. 'She needs a bit more time to think this through.' He dumped himself into the armchair, which collapsed at an angle in a burst of stuffing. 'Brilliant.'

Gemma continued her commentary. 'She's getting really wet now. Her hair's soaked already. Don't people go small quickly when they're walking away from you?'

Pacer noticed Gemma's face screw into a frown. 'What?'

'Nothing,' decided Gemma. 'Just dogs.'

Chess would have looked for Anna weeks ago but she hadn't known how to go back to her, what to say. She'd spent the time since with an ache in her chest like it was being squeezed by a lead fist, wanting to know how to be friends again. She'd tried to bury the ache by working harder at space-shifting, dimension-splitting, time-jumping, but she had discovered that misery was its own dimension and the hardest of all to escape. She'd given up any hope of finding Splinter, Box's betrayal had killed a part of her, and now she'd managed to lose the one friend she'd made outside the wharf.

But maybe this was how it had to be. Spending so much time alone meant that she had had time to think clearly, and one of the things she was certain about was that she couldn't take people with her to where she was going. Another thing was that only she could do what had to be done. Finding the Eternal and destroying it was for her alone.

Water-filled cracks in the pavement glistened like veins of glass and she stamped through a puddle. She had to find the Sages. Balthazar had told her that they were the people who knew how the universe worked and where everything was. So, it followed that they would be able to tell her where the twelve suns were one. And there, she would find the Eternal.

But she hadn't found the Sages yet. She had drifted into space with their name in her mind but without any clear idea of where to go, and she had ended up going nowhere in particular. She needed something to focus on, or something to take her close to them.

The rain showed no sign of stopping. At least Knott Street had been dry and she had had the best memories to keep her company. She had stared at that armchair for hours, for days maybe, if you added up all the hours, turning the chess piece in her hands as she did so, feeling every moulding of the horse's head. She had dug the chess piece from under the tiles of the fireplace on her first visit to Knott Street by using the cusp of the parallax bangle. The parallax bangle had been full of her blood and when she had finished with it she had cast it aside. Carelessly, perhaps. Certainly the bangle had gone when she returned, months later. But there could be many explanations for that.

Chess had lost track of how much time she had spent in the sepulchral apartment, leaving only to find food. Pacer and Gemma turning up had jolted her into action again. And now she was wet through. She wondered whether they were still there, felt an ember of tenderness glow, and quickly smothered it before it weakened her. She guessed that they would stay at the apartment until it had stopped raining. Then they would spirit through the wet darkness, back to the wharf. Or maybe Crazy Boris's. So, she'd wait until the rain had stopped and then go back to the apartment. And tomorrow, perhaps, she'd work out how to find Balthazar. He might be able to help her. He knew the vortex. She had a suspicion that he would know how to find the Sages. But he was the only one she could face; only Balthazar understood what she was up against. He knew that when you fought the Twisted Symmetry, you fought yourself. And more than that, he understood how bad it felt when you made mistakes with people.

The street lights didn't work on Knott Street. There was no electricity. If there had been, the derelicts would have been full of street rats and squatters, siphoning it off for free. So, evening fell and the street grew darker. It seemed to darken even in the time it took for her to walk down it. Her fingers followed the outline of the horse's head in her jeans pocket.

Chess was used to seeing dogs in the Undergrove. Sometimes the stray dogs or street packs had been her only companions, snuffling down the narrow ginnels, loping back to dry cellars after foraging in the rubbish-strewn back streets of the city centre.

Chess had learnt not to trust dogs; that not everything that looked like a dog *was* a dog. But the dogs in the Undergrove showed no interest in her; plainly they were not shape-shifting troopers. So, spotting one dog, two dogs, three dogs, slipping through the rain-dashed dusk was no reason to worry. Chess was barely aware of them. But when she noticed that the pack was growing, and that it appeared to be keeping pace with her along a parallel street, flashing past the far ends of the alleys she passed, Chess realised that these dogs were different. Also, she realised how swiftly she had begun to walk.

'Stupid girl,' she muttered to herself. But Chess knew that she could trust her instincts. She wasn't being stupid. Dogs didn't shadow her though the Undergrove, not normal dogs. And now that she had slowed to look, she could see that these weren't normal dogs.

They were big, with thick necks and solid shoulders, very different from the rangy, raw-boned wraiths who haunted the Undergrove. And even without street lighting, she could see that their skin had a sheen that made it look flatter and harder than skin should look. It was strange; it seemed almost metallic, yet soft. As the dogs filed into the alley, she saw their muzzles, black and gleaming, and above the muzzles, eyes that were coal-red. Dogs weren't meant to have eyes like that.

Their growls were like iron scraping and their teeth were long and glinted silver.

Chess didn't run.

There must have been at least six of them, stalking down the alley, jostling against each other in their hunger to reach her first. But Chess didn't run because she didn't have to run. There was another, easier way to escape. These dogs weren't coming for a Chess who was nervously riveted to her own world; they were coming for a Chess who had learnt to move between worlds and across dimensions.

So, Chess stood her ground and opened the time-space around her. Knott Street blurred as its dimensions separated, and this blurring began to spread into the rest of the city. Chess focused more intensely, until all boundaries between her and the city and the space beyond the city had vanished.

To anyone in the city, the metropolis would have remained the same clanking, smoking, jagged, whirling, glaring cacophony. But to Chess, now, that reality was nothing more than a skin and she was into the deeper spaces beneath. The city vanished from her and she vanished from the city. And she knew that the dogs would vanish too, stranded in the plane she had left. She would wait in the drift of time and space and emerge back into the city when it was safe.

Never before had she paid attention to sound when travelling the dimensions; never before had she any need to do so. But this time, there were sounds, like bass notes thumped from a synthesiser, bending in the drifting texture of this in-between world. Chess peered into the unstructured matrix about her and saw where the sounds came from: shapes that had a clear, definite structure, a dog structure. They moved as quick and sharp as dogs, their howls and barks warped by the distorted space, and their livid eyes were fixed on her.

This shouldn't have been happening. Dogs couldn't follow here. But these weren't ordinary dogs and with a jolt of terror that made her feel more alive than she had felt in weeks, Chess realised that these were dogs that would come for her wherever she went.

She flung herself into the nebulous slipstream, running as she reached back into the city. It came at her in phantom chunks: a strip of road with headlights hurtling, a rush of skyscraper, a clutch of power lines. And as she emerged from the deep dimensions, the city took on substance, so that she had to hurdle the cars and vault the walls which flew at her from out of the time-space flow.

And behind her came the dogs. Again, Chess saw how their bodies looked almost metallic, lithe but with a hard sheen. Their cries sharpened and they belted along the route that Chess took, snorting and bellowing like bulls.

Chess was grasping at breath. In this state, she could cover vast sections of the city in seconds, but so could the dogs. And even if they didn't run her down, she was going to smash herself to pieces on the fabric of the city if she didn't slow up. A face, laughing on a gigantic neon hoarding, whirred over her head and Chess swerved to avoid a stack of concrete pillars supporting one of the central flyovers.

The city might have looked like a smudge, but it would feel real enough if she hit it.

Chess didn't know how to throw off dogs that could hunt her like this, but she knew that she couldn't deal with this on her own.

We don't want you to be on your own now.

And suddenly, despite the terror of what was snarling behind her, Pacer's words sent a burst of energy through her soul. He was right; she didn't *have* to be on her own; she *wasn't* on her own. It might have taken the jaws of hell to make her see that, but she saw it now. She had wanted to find a way of going back to Anna, of climbing out of the misery, and now she had found it. Or it had found her. Fear had smashed all the hurt, all the heartache.

She had a friend with whom she could stand shoulder to shoulder, however lively it got. Chess just had to stay alive long enough to find her.

Thursday evening; hockey practice. Chess had a rough idea of where to look. She curved west and in a ravening pack, so did the dogs.

When travelling was as quick as thinking, you had to slow your thoughts to control where you went. Chess disconnected her thoughts, allowing the space around her to catch up with her body. She felt solid ground rush under her feet like an escalator running too fast, she was hit by the smell of damp vegetation, low branches and twigs shattered as she hurtled into the solid-state of the Lungs and as her legs shot from under her, she tumbled out of the wood and onto a pavement beneath the neon bath of the street lamps.

The air was cool from the rain that had stopped falling.

Chess remained on her back long enough to be sure that she hadn't hurt herself any more than the silver rip to the skin of her right hand which she had used to break her fall.

A hundred metres back in the woods, vegetation smashed and then there came a long, harrowing howl, answered by others. She rolled to her feet, she had to keep moving; the skin on her artificial right hand would repair itself; the skin on her throat wouldn't.

Her navigation had been as accurate as she could have hoped. Chess recognised this street. Not far ahead there was a left turn into the road where Anna's house was. She ran for that, and as she did so, she saw a long-legged figure in sports kit with a heavy kit bag across its back strolling from the opposite direction.

'Anna!' Chess could have wept with relief, if she had had the breath, if she hadn't been running so hard. She didn't stop running until she was face to face with the tall girl. With a cold lash, the rain began to fall, running off Anna's straight, black fringe.

Chess's gasps for breath were so raw she could barely speak. 'Anna, I'm so . . . so . . .'

Anna put a finger over Chess's lips. 'Sorry,' she whispered. 'And so am I. I'm sorry too.'

For a moment, Chess felt hot with an insane happiness. Then, fifty metres behind her, the bushes at the edge of the road exploded open and the dogs pounded into the road, snarling, red eyes wild.

'Ah.' Anna cocked an eyebrow. 'It's business as usual, I see.'

'Sorry,' repeated Chess, blinking rainwater out of her eyes.

'No need to say that, OK? You're my friend.' Her eyes narrowed as she looked over Chess's shoulder at what was heading their way. 'Nice pets. But if I were you, I'd stick to hamsters in future.'

'What do we do?' panted Chess. She could hear claws scraping over tarmac.

Anna considered the matter for a tenth of a second. 'Run,' she whispered.

They ran, Anna leading the way off the road and back into the woods. Chess knew that this would take them onto the track that came out at the bottom of the Ledwards' long garden, by the summerhouse. Even with the kit bag which sounded full enough to be heavy, Anna's long legs took her through the trees so fast that Chess had to sprint to keep up.

Anna charged out of the woods and slid to a standstill in the wet grass by the summerhouse. The bag was off her back and she ripped it open.

'How many?' she demanded, breathless but calm, just as Chess had known she would be.

'Six, I think.'

Anna snatched out her goal-keeper's body armour and began to strap it on. 'Ever played hockey?' she asked as she yanked the shin pads tight.

Anna was calm, determined, but Chess found it hard to hold back the fear as she stood in the pouring rain and death came slinking out of the wood line. The growls were low, deep enough to turn her stomach to water. 'I've never played hockey,' she said, barely hearing her own voice.

'Now's your big chance.'

Something swooped towards her and she caught the hockey stick that Anna had thrown.

Anna took another stick from the bag and hefted it in her gloved hands. The dogs had gathered in a line, six pairs of eyes smouldering, throats rumbling. Anna stepped forwards, putting herself between Chess and the dogs. Her voice dropped. 'What kind of dogs *are* these, Chess?'

She noticed the metallic sheen, the unnatural bulk. Red eyes narrowed on her and lips drew back revealing teeth which glinted, long and sharp enough to shred the darkness. When the growls rose in pitch, ripping through the hiss of rain, Anna spun the stick in her hands, arcing it by her left shoulder and then her right. It hummed through the air. 'These aren't like dogs at all,' she murmured, sizing up the opposition. 'They're machines.'

The dogs were ready to attack.

'I'm sorry, Anna,' shivered Chess. 'I shouldn't have ... '

'No more apologies,' whispered Anna, focusing on the creatures ahead. The rain ran off her helmet in streams. 'There's no referee.' She looked at Chess and actually smiled. 'My favourite kind of game.'

Claws raking the earth, the dogs charged.

The first two came straight for Anna. They belted out of the darkness and sprang. Chess had seen how fast Anna was with a sword, and she knew how quick her reactions were with a hockey stick, but still she couldn't track the movement. She heard wood smash against one dog's head, then saw Anna drop to one knee and swing up, catching the other dog square under its jaw. The first dog careered into a wooden wall of the summerhouse, senseless. The other sprinted howling into the woods.

But now Anna's leg was in the mouth of another hound, its head shaking as if to rip off the shin pad its gleaming fangs had fastened to. Chess would have stepped in, but one of the blood-eyed creatures was loping towards her, skulking, taking its time, separating her from Anna.

Chess heard the savage grunts as two more dogs tried to take Anna down. Anna drove the haft of the stick down into the skull of the dog at her leg, splitting the metallic casing perfectly, turned her shoulder into one of the leaping beasts and struck up at the other. She struck up so hard that the dog was driven into the summerhouse, its own momentum sending it crashing through the glass.

But with the weight of the huge hound on her chest, its jaws clamped to her left shoulder, Anna was falling sideways. Even then, she was still fighting. With both hands on her stick, she slogged it across the back of the dog that had been approaching Chess. There was a snap. The stick broke, but so did the dog's spine. It collapsed, forelegs jerking like broken clockwork whilst its hind legs were motionless.

Anna was on her back. Her left shoulder was on fire. The dog's paws were pressed into her chest. It lifted its blood-streaked muzzle and looked down at her, eyes burning, silver fangs glistening. Then its head shot forwards and its jaws fastened on the bars of the cage that protected her face. Even though the metal blocked the long teeth, she felt as if her head was about to be shaken off. Then she sensed breath on the exposed skin of her throat.

The dog lifted its head, drew back its lips and snarled.

That was when Chess swung her stick like she was striking a baseball. It slammed into the side of the creature's skull so hard that the whole head assembly was smashed from its neck. The dog head went spinning though one of the remaining summerhouse windows with a smash. Then there was silence, apart from the falling rain.

'You should join the team,' gasped Anna, pulling off the helmet and sitting up. Rainwater mixed with the blood that was leaking from her left shoulder, running down her arm.

'Are you OK?' Chess knelt down.

Anna looked at the bodies that littered the lawn. 'Better than them,' she said.

'Anna!' Mr Ledward's voice resounded from the far end of the lawn, where the house was. 'Anna!'

'Oh no,' groaned Anna. She stood up slowly, pressing her hand to the wound on her shoulder. Blood seeped between her fingers. 'Just stay here, OK? I'm going to have to distract him.'

'Alright,' said Chess, who was more worried about the injury to Anna than what her father would have to say about his smashed windows and the dog bodies.

Anna's blue eyes were intense as she said, 'Just stay here.'

Chess shrugged. 'I've got nowhere to go.' She wiped rain from her face.

'Anna.' The voice was nearer now.

'It's alright, Dad,' Anna shouted back and she walked away.

Chess prodded one of the bodies with her foot. Despite the metal sheen, the skin was pliable: not as soft as normal skin, maybe as tough as heavy-duty polythene, the sort that went white but wouldn't tear when you pulled it. Some sort of warp engineered, metal-flesh alloy. But no protection against an expertly wielded hockey stick.

The rain had stopped. Chess rested against a wooden wall and listened to the water dripping from the trees in the wood. There were no voices that she could hear but a light had come on in the kitchen and there was movement: Anna sitting in a chair, sleeve rolled up, her father inspecting her shoulder.

Chess watched unblinking. It was such a different world, it was hard to believe it was separated by nothing more than bricks and glass.

Chess's idle musing was halted by sounds: the snap of twigs, the rustle of leaves, a fall of breath. Although she couldn't see what was happening round the back of the summerhouse, where the trees were, she knew there was movement. And this wasn't one person, or one thing; the same sounds were repeating, as if there was a gathering.

That was when she made herself look right and saw eyes in the tree line, red eyes, maybe four or five pairs, all watching her. Instinctively, Chess backed away.

A low growl from behind made her stumble round. Two dogs had sloped round the corner of the summerhouse, heads low, teeth bared.

Chess knew that there was no vanishing from these creatures, and there were so many of them now, slipping out of the trees and weaving towards her. She still had the hockey stick in her hand but suddenly it was very heavy. And anyway, she couldn't fight like Anna.

Chess didn't cry out. She cast a last glance at the warmth

and light of the kitchen and the figures within. And now she realised, in a way she had never appreciated before, why Anna had not risked her with Ravillious; there was no way Chess was going to call Anna into this circle of death.

The stick slipped from her hand. 'Kill me,' Chess whispered to the dogs, 'but you won't have my friend.'

The darkness closed in, isolating her in a world of ember-red eyes and long, silver teeth.

'Chess.'

She ignored the voice; barely registered it. It could only have been her imagination; a last desperate illusion conjured by her mind to make dying easier.

'Chess.'

She hesitated. 'Splinter?'

'Chess, come on.'

It was Splinter, only ten metres away, standing on the lawn in a cloud of mist. He held out his hand.

The dogs were drawing closer, but suddenly they had become no more real than spectres. For the second time that night, a coursing happiness surged through Chess's body.

'I knew you'd come for me. I saw you looking.' Chess stumbled forwards. Terror gave way to a choking joy. 'I knew I could trust you, Splinter.'

But still, when she was only a couple of metres away, she hesitated. The last time she had seen Splinter had been just before the snatch squad had come for them on Surapoor; she had never forgotten the look he had given her, a sad, searching kind of look. And there was the same sort of look on his face now.

'Everything's alright, isn't it?' she asked.

Then Splinter smiled in a way that made the dogs and the darkness vanish. 'Yes, Chess, everything's alright.'

'Anna?'

'We'll come back for Anna when the dogs have gone.' There was tenderness in his eyes.

Chess put out her hand and felt Splinter grasp it in his own. He pulled her towards him and she went willingly. This was what she had wanted for so long, what she had barely dared to hope for. But they were together now and this was the best feeling in the world. Chess smiled at Splinter and he smiled back at her. Still holding his hand, she walked into the mist. At last, everything was going to be alright.